"Don't You Wa[nt...]"

"Yes, of course I do," Travis said. He had come for absolution, realizing that he had been wrong in treating her so badly that she felt she needed to quit. He had thought she'd welcome him, but instead she appeared wary. He knew her attitude shouldn't irritate him but it did. He wished she'd just accept his peace offering and be done with it. "That's what I'm paying you for."

She took a closer look at the plant he'd brought. A large card was attached to one of its branches, explaining all about its care and feeding. Too bad Travis hadn't come with a card, she thought. "Does this mean that you want me to come back to work? Or is it your quaint way of saying goodbye?"

"I'd like you to come back."

It was a turning point in his life.

Dear Reader:

SILHOUETTE DESIRE is an exciting new line of contemporary romances from Silhouette Books. During the past year, many Silhouette readers have written in telling us what other types of stories they'd like to read from Silhouette, and we've kept these comments and suggestions in mind in developing SILHOUETTE DESIRE.

DESIREs feature all of the elements you like to see in a romance, plus a more sensual, provocative story. So if you want to experience all the excitement, passion and joy of falling in love, then SILHOUETTE DESIRE is for you.

For more details write to:

Jane Nicholls
Silhouette Books
PO Box 236
Thornton Road
Croydon
Surrey
CR9 3RU

MARIE NICOLE
Last Year's Hunk

Silhouette Desire

Originally Published by Silhouette Books
division of
Harlequin Enterprises Ltd.

First published in Great Britain in 1986 by Silhouette Books, 15–16 Brook's Mews, London W1A 1DR

© Marie Rydzynski-Ferrarella 1986

Silhouette, Silhouette Desire and Colophon are Trade Marks of Harlequin Enterprises B.V.

ISBN 0 373 50432 2

22–0986

Printed and bound in Great Britain by Cox & Wyman Ltd, Reading

MARIE NICOLE

is a natural romance writer because her own life has been so romantic. She met her husband-to-be in tenth grade and began dating him in college. The first time he kissed her he made the room fade away, and things have only gotten better for them since.

Other Silhouette Books by Marie Nicole

Silhouette Desire

Tried and True
Buyer Beware
Through Laughter and Tears
Grand Theft: Heart
A Woman of Integrity
Country Blue

To Bonnie Stone Sexton,
and all the trees that died
in the last twenty-five years
so that we could write to each other.

One

⸻

"You're C. J. Parker?"

Travis McQuade's normally calm, low voice displayed obvious confusion mixed with annoyance as it filled his business manager's wood-paneled office. A woman, of all things! What was Peter thinking of?

How could he accept a woman as a personal manager, feeling the way he felt? It was absolutely impossible. Travis shoved his hands into his jeans as he circled her.

"Yes, I'm C. J. Parker." C.J. turned her head, watching him until he moved behind her. He certainly wasn't behaving the way her clients usually did. But, then, he wasn't like her other clients had been. Most of them were well settled into their careers. He was a newcomer to the Hollywood scene, albeit probably the biggest sensation of the decade. He was also every bit as good-looking as his pictures. Without any makeup.

"But you're a woman."

C.J. didn't know if there was a complaint or just surprise in his voice.

"Nice of you to notice," she said dryly. She glanced at Peter Ashley accusingly. What was going on here? Was this why she had packed so quickly and flown three thousand miles through some of the worst turbulence she ever hoped to experience? Maybe she should just have come home and taken that vacation the way she had originally planned.

Travis ran his hand through his thick chestnut hair. A bit of humidity was in the air, and his hair was curling badly. He had to find time for a haircut, he thought absently.

He looked at the woman who was patiently bearing up to his rather blatant scrutiny. She was a short, pert blond with shoulder-length hair that was having trouble deciding which way to fall. She was dressed in a smart business suit that seemed to emphasize her femininity rather than detract from it. Since she had entered the room five minutes ago and chirped the most enthusiastic hello he had ever heard, she had made him think of a hummingbird, hovering in the air, debating what direction to dart off in next.

"You'll forgive me, Miss Parker, but the last thing in the world I need in my life is another woman. My life is filled to overflowing with women. Short women, tall women, young, old, all with autograph books in their hands."

God, had he really just said that? He didn't even sound like himself anymore. Who would ever have thought he'd be complaining about being in demand? He had dreamed of having fans, of people wanting to see him act....

But that was before things had gotten out of hand.

He realized that he was tired. Really tired. He didn't mind the daily grind. And after the initial thrill and disbelief had worn off, it had become that. He was grateful, in a town where eighty-five percent of the actors were unemployed, to be working at all, much less as the star of a popular series. Granted, at times the episodes were downright silly, but he liked the crew who worked with him. And the show paid the bills rather handsomely.

It was the rest of it that bothered him. How had it all gotten so out of control? Every time he turned around there were photographers ready to snap his picture, or women offering him keys to their apartments. Or mailing him provocative pictures of themselves. He couldn't go anywhere without attracting a crowd. If he went out for a box of cereal, someone popped up out of the blue to write a feature about his favorite brand.

At first he had taken it all in stride. It was new, exciting. But after a while it had become too much. He'd begun to feel trapped. Naturally shy, he'd begun to withdraw. He'd been forced to adopt a life of seclusion. Success had caged him. He hated the thought of being caged. And it wasn't even the kind of success he had wanted. He didn't want to be regarded as the handsome star of a beefcake series. He wanted to be regarded as an *actor*. A *good* actor.

At times he thought he was going a little crazy. How many struggling actors would have given everything they had just to trade places with him? And here he was complaining.

He realized that C.J. was talking again, and had been for at least a minute now. She held out her hands, palms up, then turned them over. "See, no autograph book. And look, nothing up my sleeve." Elaborately she shook it. "The only place I'll ask for your autograph is on my paycheck," she promised.

There was a stubborn look on Travis's face. C.J. looked at Peter. "You didn't tell him, I take it, to expect a woman?" Why the fact that she was a woman should bother Travis McQuade was beyond her. The man's popularity was built on the throbbing hearts of women from eight to eighty. Did a chauvinistic heart actually beat beneath that shy, easy smile? Another legend dies hard, she thought dryly.

Peter's answer was directed to Travis instead of C.J. "You asked for the best," he said helplessly. "You didn't specify anything beyond that."

"Why were you expecting a man?" C.J. asked. "The term 'personal manager' is genderless."

"Most women don't use initials," Travis said.

"Most women don't have a name like Clementine Jean," she answered.

"Clementine?" he echoed in disbelief.

She nodded, accustomed to the quizzically humorous stares she invariably received when she admitted to the awful name. "My father's favorite movie was *My Darling Clementine*, with Henry Fonda—"

"And Victor Mature," Travis concluded. "I've seen it."

"My father will approve of my working for such a well-rounded man." C.J. grinned.

"You're not working for me yet," Travis said, stubbornly holding out.

He realized that he was being unreasonable. After all, he had agreed with Peter that he needed a personal manager. But nonetheless, he was having trouble accepting all this. Lately he had felt that life was closing in on him from all sides. On the one hand, he craved the privacy he no longer had. On the other, he needed to invite someone else into his life to take care of the things he no longer had time to tend to. Details kept escaping him. There just weren't enough hours in the day for him to handle everything. He was used to handling everything, used to being in control of his life. But stardom was pulling the reins away from him.

It was still hard to believe that three years ago he'd been living on catsup soup, barely making a living by working as an extra in movies. Now his face adorned all the popular magazines, and *TV Guide* wanted to run a feature on him.

The pressure of doing a weekly series and being "this year's hunk," a title he had held since the series began, was beginning to take its toll.

"Look, I'm sure you're very nice, but—"

"Yes, I am," C.J. readily agreed. "But nice isn't the point here. If you want nice, get a cocker spaniel. I'm competent." She turned to Peter for support.

Peter couldn't nod fast enough. "Baxter Tremayne says she's *very* competent."

Travis cast a dubious eye in C.J.'s direction. Baxter Tremayne was one of the few people in Hollywood who never had a bad word to say about anyone. The fact that the man had given her a recommendation didn't convince Travis of her worth.

He leaned back against the windowsill, his palms spread out behind him, balancing his weight. Women were part of his problem, not part of the solution. His female fans had him cornered, both figuratively and otherwise. He couldn't get any substantial acting roles because of his popularity on the show. The Nielsen ratings had gone through the roof, and everyone in the acting community, as well as outside it, equated Travis McQuade with Paris Cassidy. According to his agent, no one would even consider him for any other type of role.

Although his female fans had initially been the source of his success, they were now also the source of his stagnation. And fans were known for their fickleness. Tomorrow, another hunk could appear on the horizon, another heartthrob to catch their fantasy. Without any further acting credentials, he would be left high and dry. His career would vanish as quickly as it had materialized.

All he had ever wanted to do was act. The lead in *Paris Cassidy, Man with a Gun* had fallen into his lap, and suddenly he had become a sensation. So much so that his agent urged him not to rock the boat every time he mentioned taking on a role against type. Berenstein kept saying things like, "Eric Fontaine never had to act." But he didn't want to be Eric Fontaine. Eric Fontaine had wound up an empty drunk, searching for the fountain of youth and playing roles that were far too young for him. Travis wanted to be Laurence Olivier.

Maybe he wanted too much, he thought disparagingly.

What he knew he *didn't* want, though, was a woman coming into his life and taking over. The series itself took up too much of his time. He was on the set from dawn until dusk five, often six, days a week. That left everything else up in the air during the shooting season. Phone calls went unanswered. Appointments were forgotten. He wasn't used to conducting his life so sloppily. It had taken him a full year to admit that to himself, and six more months before he voiced it to anyone else. He needed someone to help him. It wasn't easy, asking for help. It was even less easy asking it of a woman.

C.J. looked to Peter. "Am I getting the silent treatment, or is he thinking?"

She had just spent five and a half hours on a plane; she was suffering from jet lag, and she was just the slightest bit irritable. Besides, she was eager to get back to her apartment to see if the boy she was paying had remembered to water her Ficus benjamina.

Peter had called her last week with his "dilemma." It had been like a ray of sunshine on a rainy, wet New York afternoon. Her present client, a renowned actress of the Broadway stage, had been sailing smoothly for some time now. Too smoothly. And while that pointed to C.J.'s efficiency, it also contributed to her boredom. She needed a challenge, something to sink her teeth into. She thrived on making order out of chaos. And she had more than welcomed the chance to come home to a paying position. Her bags had already been packed when Peter called, and she had already given her notice that very morning, intending to come home and think about her next move.

She turned her attention to Travis, who was still frowning thoughtfully. She'd had more than a score of clients, and none of them had ever complained because she was a woman. She took Travis's reluctance as a personal challenge and dug in. She was quite good at what she did. Past clients swore by her. Why was this man being so reluctant? Was he just a chauvinist, or was there something more to it?

At twenty-eight C.J. had the comfort of knowing that her abilities were very much in demand. This town was filled to overflowing with people who couldn't keep their lives any straighter than the rumpled sheets on their beds.

And Travis McQuade was one man who could use her talents, if everything that Peter had told her was true. She had been relentless in her questioning. She always liked to know what she was getting into. Travis did look a little bit ragged around the edges, now that she stopped to notice. And his hair was too long. Probably couldn't find the time to see his hairdresser. Yes, he needed her, she decided.

So why didn't the big jerk see that?

"I'm sorry, Miss Parker, but I'm afraid it just won't work out," Travis said, straightening up and moving away from the windowsill.

"Why?" she wanted to know.

She certainly wasn't making this any easier, he thought. He stood next to her now, six foot two looking down at five three at best. And that was in heels.

"I need someone... professional," he finally said, dismissing what Peter had said about her being the best. Peter meant well, but he had obviously been taken in by someone's idea of a joke.

It had to be a joke. She looked too young, too enthusiastic, too everything, Travis concluded. A personal manager, in his mind, was someone who looked reserved and somber and very, very efficient. C.J. gave the impression of a hurricane about to happen.

"I can give you a reference list that would make your eyes pop out," C.J. told him, feeling as if her reputation were at stake here.

He shook his head firmly. "No, don't bother. I won't be needing you." He'd find some way to handle this himself. He should have never given in to his moment of weakness and talked to Peter. Only weak people needed help in managing their own affairs, like confused children.

"I'm very good at my job, Mr. McQuade," C.J. insisted.

Travis gave her a long, last look—or so he thought. "I'm sure you are, but—"

"There is no but," she answered with a smile. "Just a pure and simple fact. And you need me. Also a pure and simple fact."

"I do, do I?" He crossed his arms across his chest and regarded her challengingly.

She had seen that kind of look before. It was forged out of steel. But it could be melted down. She didn't let it faze her. "Yes." She smiled. "Very much, from what Peter says."

She had to be one of the most brazen women he had ever encountered. "You make it sound as if you're in the business of performing miracles, rather than just being a personal manager."

"Not miracles," she answered lightly. "I just right wrongs, then go on my way."

She practically sparkled, he thought. Just like a Roman candle before it went off.

"Kind of like Zorro," she added as an after-thought.

"Been Zorro long?" he asked, leaning against Peter's desk.

"Five years."

Her answer surprised him. "Started in elementary school, did you?"

C.J. laughed. It wasn't one of those tinkling, mild little laughs that the starlets used in order not to ruin their carefully applied makeup. She laughed as if someone were tickling her. It was an honest laugh. It showed him that she really was highly amused by him. He wasn't all that sure he liked it. "I'm not as young as I look."

"And just how old are you, if you don't mind my asking?" He would never ask a woman her age. Not normally. But there was just something about this one that egged him on.

"I don't mind your asking if you don't mind my not answering." She paused, mischief in her eyes. "I'm old enough to have been working for five years. And I have five years of references to offer you." There was pride in her voice.

"Can't keep a steady job, eh?" He was baiting her, but he couldn't help himself. There was something about her that made him want to test her. He felt just the slightest bit threatened by her. Or was it the situation itself? He realized that at the moment, he might very well be his worst enemy. But a lifetime of guarding his privacy and taking pride in his independence was disappearing right in front of his eyes, and it was a difficult thing to stand.

"Can't keep a boring job," she countered. "Once everything is back on the right track I get restless. I don't like life to be predictable. I feel like something's missing then. And you, McQuade," she said, not mincing any words, "are a challenge."

"Oh, and just when did my life get on the top-ten list of disasters?" he asked, turning toward Peter. He was being defensive, and he knew it. His life certainly wasn't a disaster, but the peripheral details could use a good deal of straightening up. He needed someone to handle the small things so he could concentrate on things that were of greater importance to him—like where his career was headed. If he didn't reclaim the helm soon, he might very well drift into a channel he had no desire to remain in. The thought unnerved him. "Look, Peter," he said suddenly, abandoning the discussion, "I've got to go. I'll call you sometime and we can talk about this." It was Sunday, the only day he had to himself lately, and he didn't want to waste his precious free time arguing.

Peter hardly got a chance to open his mouth before he shut it again.

"I talk, too," C.J. said, cutting in. Her voice was a little more gentle than it had been.

"I'm sure you do. Constantly, if these few minutes are any indication, but I—" Travis began.

"Will give me a try, won't you?" she asked.

Suddenly the mischief was gone from her face. She didn't look quite so young anymore. What she did look was sincere. "Sunday is a really terrible time to go looking for another job. Especially when you have to take your suitcases along on the interview." Her serious look dissolved into a wink.

It was a very beguiling wink. It belonged to a very self-assured woman who was appealing despite her overconfidence. Or maybe because of it.

No, don't start getting soft now, he warned himself. You don't need a woman in your life, complicating things. But he did need someone, he argued with himself.

She was smiling at him as if she were reading his thoughts. She probably claimed to be clairvoyant, as well as efficient, he thought sarcastically.

He was vacillating. He should have his head examined, he thought. This was really insane. But there was something about her sheer grit that impressed him. "All right. I suppose it won't hurt to give you a trial run."

C.J. raised her right hand. "Absolutely painless, I promise."

He had his doubts about that.

Well, that settled it, she thought with a smile. She stuck out her hand. When he didn't take it immediately, she took his in hers. "I'll come by your place in the morning to start getting you in order."

He wasn't sure he liked the sound of that, but he held his tongue. He had said he'd give her a try, and it was only fair that he keep his word. His word meant a lot to him. At times it felt like all he had.

She turned toward a very relieved-looking Peter and asked, "Could you call me a cab?"

"You don't want me to take you home?" he asked, not all that eager to get embroiled in the Sunday afternoon traffic again. One grueling trip to the airport was about all he could endure.

C.J. grinned. "You've done quite enough for one day."

Travis was about to walk out of the office, when something stopped him. Oh, what the hell? "Where are you staying?"

Her eyes turned in his direction. She looked as if she had been expecting him to come through all the time. He wondered if she kept a score card on the number of times she turned out to be right. "My apartment. It's just a few miles down on Wilshire."

He motioned for her to join him. "I'm heading down that way. I'll drop you off. You have suitcases, I take it?"

Peter groaned. "Does she have suitcases . . ."

C.J. shot him a warning look, then turned her attention back to Travis. "They're right out here, in the outer office." She led the way. "I was at the soda machine when you came in," she told him.

He stopped picking up suitcases to stare at her blankly. Where had that come from? His expression said as much.

"That's why you didn't see me on your way in," she clarified.

"If I had, I might have had a fighting chance," Travis said, more to himself than to her, as he picked up four of the suitcases.

Not a chance, C.J. thought, picking up the last suitcase.

"Don't you think it was a wee bit presumptuous of you to come out here with five suitcases before I agreed to hire you?" Travis challenged, making his way out the door and to the elevator.

"No," C.J. answered cheerfully, following him. I was coming home, anyway, she thought, but she kept that part to herself.

Two

—

C.J. gave Travis the address of her apartment building as they rode down in the elevator. His car was parked right out front.

"Interesting car," C.J. said, looking at the sky-blue Ferrari. "I've never ridden in a car shaped like a bullet." She watched him as he made several attempts to arrange her luggage so it would fit in the trunk.

"I'm afraid you're going to have to ride with two suitcases on your lap," he told her.

"I guess sports car enthusiasts don't believe in trunks, do they?"

He gave her a cryptic look. "People who own Ferraris travel light."

"That's probably because they don't have enough money left over after paying for the car to buy any luggage," she commented softly, but loud enough for him to hear.

The car didn't suit him, she thought. Its long, sleek lines were racy, flashy. A car like this was meant for someone who felt the need to draw attention to himself, someone who needed to boost his ego. From what she had found out from Peter, that wasn't Travis. He was levelheaded and felt somewhat uncomfortable about the sensation he had created. Maybe the car represented another side of him. Well, she'd find out soon enough, she promised herself.

"We're going to have to travel heavy," he muttered, handing her her overnight case. He took the remaining suitcase and loaded it into the front seat, on the passenger side.

"I take it that people who own Ferraris also don't believe in friends."

He cocked his head and stared at her, obviously confused.

She nodded toward the back of the car. "There's no back seat."

"Just friends they want next to them. Look—" He stopped abruptly. One suitcase was precariously balanced on the seat, half in, half out, "I can always call you a cab."

"No," she said cheerfully, giving the suitcase a shove, then placing the overnight case squarely on top. "You'll do fine."

"Thank you." The tone was ten degrees below zero.

She gave him what he thought was the softest smile he had ever seen. "You're welcome."

The woman's got gall, all right, he thought.

Obviously the makers of small sports cars also didn't want their passengers getting too comfortable, C.J. thought as she got in through the passenger door, pushing the suitcases as far aside as she could. Her legs were almost straight out in front of her. As she moved, attempting to find a more comfortable position, her skirt rode up. She tugged at it, but her cramped position made it difficult. Out of the corner of her eye, she saw Travis watching her, a bemused smile on his face.

"I never sat in a ladle before," she told him. "Takes a bit of getting used to."

He gave her a meaningful look, then turned forward. "A lot of that's going around lately."

There was an intensity in his voice that made C.J. uneasy. It passed quickly, but she could see that this wasn't going to be easy. But, then, she thrived on challenge.

"You'll get used to me," C.J. laughed. "I'll grow on you."

Like fungus, he thought.

"And by then I'll be gone," she concluded.

Promises, promises.

C.J. shifted in her seat again. The luggage was pressing against her legs, cutting off her circulation.

Get your mind off your discomfort and on your work, C.J., she ordered herself.

"Okay," she said, and Travis got the uneasy feeling that he had just heard the opening shot being fired at the Indianapolis 500. "In order to get rolling, I'm going to need a complete list of everyone you deal with. Names, addresses, phone numbers," she said, tapping the top of her suitcase as she enumerated the items.

He didn't like the sound of this. He felt as if he were being interrogated. "Are you a personal manager or the FBI?"

"The FBI doesn't care who your hairdresser is. I do." She shifted in her seat and reached over the two suitcases to touch his hair. The chestnut mane had more than a passing acquaintance with the top of his collar. "You do have a hairdresser, don't you?"

He scowled. "I don't have a choice. It comes with the territory." He was obviously annoyed with her questions.

C.J. sank back in her seat again. The smoldering annoyance on his face puzzled her. If he didn't want her suggestions, why had he asked for a personal manager to begin with? "Haven't been to see him in a while, have you?" She struggled to pull out a pad from her purse. When she finally yanked it free, she made herself a note. "I'll get him to see you . . ."

Travis set his jaw stubbornly, making his profile look, C.J. thought, as if it had been lovingly carved out of granite by an enamored sculptress. "I don't need to see my hairdresser."

"You need a haircut," C.J. contradicted.

She sounded sweet, yet there was no mistaking the confident assessment in her voice. This was just the tip of the iceberg. She was going to take charge of his life. It irritated him. "I can decide when I need my hair cut."

C.J. tried to put away her pad, then gave up. The suitcases were just too much of an obstacle. Was he going to be like that, too? Was he going to block her every move? "Your decision," she said patiently, "is overdue. If your hair gets any longer, you won't need a hairdresser, you'll need a lawn mower."

Patience, Travis, he cautioned himself. You don't want to throw away your whole career by killing this woman. Even if it would be justifiable homicide.

"So tell me, Clem," he said evenly. C.J. winced as he unknowingly tagged her with the nickname that had haunted her elementary school days. "What made you decide to take up meddling professionally?"

He was testing her, C.J. thought. Well, if he thought he could get her to quit before she even started, he was in for a surprise.

"I discovered that there was money to be made in helping successful but harried people establish order in their lives. Freed of the weight of annoying details, my clients have gone on to become even more successful," she replied easily, staring straight ahead as Wilshire Boulevard passed by. There was too much traffic to attempt further eye contact with him. She contented herself with looking at the road. "I like getting things in order. I like chaos, too," she said.

"It figures," he mutterd as he made a left turn. "That last comment makes absolutely no sense."

"Oh, but it does." By now he wasn't surprised that she contradicted him. "If there were no chaos, there'd be no need to restore order. It would be there all the time. Where there's chaos, there's a need for order. And I bring it." It sounded simple enough. But it confused the hell out of him.

"And on the First Day," Travis intoned in a false baritone voice, "Clem created order, and it was good."

Patience was something C.J. had developed a long, long time ago. It hadn't been easy, but she'd nurtured it until she became quite good at it. "It's not nice to make fun of the Creator, or there's no telling what I might do on the second day."

Well, at least she had a sense of humor, he thought. Maybe he should just make the best of it. He turned to look at the woman by his side. "You come on pretty strong, you know."

"Only when I meet resistance," she said quickly, then reconsidered. She smiled a bit ruefully. "Sorry. Training."

"Where did you get your training? Marine boot camp?"

She laughed. She was going to enjoy this assignment.

It was that same light, merry laugh he had heard in the office. It was, he realized, quite appealing. And quite infectious.

"No, at home," she told him. "I had five very headstrong brothers."

"Bet they were sorry," he muttered under his breath, but she heard him.

"At times I guess they were. But you see, I was the oldest. Mom died when Albie was born. I had to grow up fast. At nine, to be exact. You don't have much time to go about things slow and easy when you're trying to raise five brothers and go to school at the same time."

The small look into her past tempered Travis's feelings about her. He pulled over to the curb. For a second, as he looked at her, he thought he could almost see the very young girl she had been. He'd bet she had been overbearing even then.

"You're used to having your own way, aren't you?" he said, looking at her firm chin.

"Pretty much so," she admitted.

"So am I." There was no misunderstanding his meaning.

"You're the boss," she told him. But from the way she said it Travis got the distinct impression that she was only humoring him. Nonetheless, he seized on her statement.

"That's right. And I'll stay the boss if this thing is to work."

"It'll work," she promised without hesitation. She leveled her gaze at him, and for the first time he noticed that she had the most incredibly green eyes he had ever seen. Like the liquid green fire in the heart of a perfect emerald. Fire could be very dangerous if it wasn't harnessed. "But you *are* going to have to cooperate, you know," she answered.

"I've never been uncooperative," he replied, growing infinitely aware of her. She was wearing perfume. Did hellcats wear perfume? Must be a new trend.

"Good. By all means, let's keep it that way."

A burly, balding doorman opened her door and took the smaller suitcase from her lap, then assisted her out of the car.

"Hello, Jake."

"Welcome home, Miss C.J.," the doorman said, smiling pleasantly. "How was your—"

C.J. looked over her shoulder and realized that Jake was gaping at Travis, who had just gotten out of the car. "Trip, Jake, trip," she said, supplying the last word as she pulled the second suitcase out.

"Travis McQuade."

"Yes, he certainly is." C.J. laughed. "Mr. Travis McQuade, Jake Whitney, a fan of yours, as you can see."

The introduction seemed to bring the stocky man out of his trance. "Yes, yes, a great fan. Here, let me." He picked up the suitcases Travis was taking out of the trunk of the car. Jake placed one under each arm before grabbing the other two. C.J. picked up the last. "Tell me," the doorman said, never taking his eyes from Travis, "do you actually do all your own stunts?"

Travis was used to the kind of look he saw in the doorman's eyes. It was sheer adulation. "Yes, I do," Travis answered. "Got several cracked ribs to prove it."

C.J. glanced down the block and saw two women pointing in their direction. "Uh-oh. I think I see a couple of people who might be interested in seeing your cracked ribs and anything else you'd care to show."

Not only was she impossible to talk to, Travis realized, she was also impossible to understand. "What?"

"C'mon," C.J. said, grabbing his arm as the women's pace quickened. "I think you need to retreat."

"I could have just as easily retreated into my car," he told her as they rode up to her apartment. Jake had insisted on helping them to her door. That meant there were five suitcases, one large doorman, Travis and C.J. crammed into one small elevator. "Easier, probably," Travis amended.

He was very aware of the fact that her body was pressed close to his. Because of the limited space, there was nowhere else for her to go. She felt soft, he thought, a hint of a sensual response nipping at his consciousness. A soft gangbuster.

"I thought maybe we needed to talk a bit more," C.J. pointed out, explaining why she had grabbed his hand and pulled him along. She didn't want to tell him the real reason she had done what she had. When she had seen the look on those two women's faces, she'd gotten the impression of jackals moving in for the kill. She had no idea why, but she felt as if she had to protect him. Wouldn't he love to hear that? she thought.

Meanwhile Travis felt that he'd had quite enough of Miss Clementine Jean Parker for one day, but he knew by now that it was useless to argue. He'd save his energy for bigger things. He just knew there would be bigger things looming on the horizon shortly.

"All right, have it your way. We'll talk."

She had heard friendlier tones, she thought, opening the door to her apartment. Jake deposited the suitcases right inside.

"Thank you, Jake," C.J. said pointedly when the large man made no effort to leave.

Travis dug into the pocket of his faded jeans and pulled out a five-dollar bill. But as he went to press it into the doorman's hand, Jake backed away.

"Oh, no thank you, sir." Jake backed out of the room. "And don't worry," he promised. "I won't tell anyone you're here."

"Wouldn't want to jeopardize your reputation," Travis said dryly, looking at C.J.

C.J. was already busy pulling sheets off her living room furniture. Was he implying that he thought no man had ever been in her apartment? She decided to handle the situation lightly. "You couldn't jeopardize anyone's reputation. Paris Cassidy is a man of honor, remember?"

Did she confuse him with his screen persona, too? he wondered. He had gotten so tired of people forgetting who he was. There were times when he grew very resentful of Paris Cassidy, even though he had tried to infuse the series hero with some of his own qualities and characteristics.

"And so, I hear tell, are you," she finished. "There." She folded the last sheet and dropped it on the coffee table. "Now it looks less like a mausoleum."

"More like a fun house," he commented as he looked around. The room was done entirely in modern—or was it futuristic?—furniture. He had never been much on interior decorating. She had furniture with amoebalike characteristics. He brushed against the dark chocolate sofa and it undulated. He looked at her quizzically.

"Water sofa. Maximum comfort," she assured him. "Have a seat. I'd like to offer you a drink, but all I have at the moment is scotch. Or water."

He remained standing, eyeing the sofa dubiously as it came to rest again.

"Scotch and water will be fine." He had a feeling he was going to need something if he was to remain in her company.

C.J. walked toward her kitchen. "Scotch and water it is—oh!"

Travis turned quickly, ready to see some sort of disaster. In her single word, she had expressed utter surprise and despair simultaneously. "What's the matter?"

"Doggone that kid," she muttered. "Just look at this."

"This" was a six foot Ficus benjamina that was stationed at the entrance to her kitchen. C.J. held up a limp branch as if it were the hand of an ailing friend. It certainly was ailing.

Anger and despair flushed her cheeks. "I left him the key to my apartment so he'd water Ben regularly, and just look at this."

"Ben?"

She acted as if he were asking an unusual question. "Plants do better when you relate to them. I can't relate to anything unless it has a name."

"Whatever you say." She was beginning to sound odder by the minute. "I think I'll have that scotch now. Skip the water." He tried to move past her to get into the kitchen. The opening was too small to accommodate both their bodies and the ailing plant at the same time.

As his body brushed against C.J.'s, she pressed her back against the counter. It did no good. Contact was made and fully registered.

"I . . . um . . . sorry," he muttered.

C.J. temporarily forgot that her benjamina was on its deathbed. Something else was happening to her that was more important than falling leaves. She looked up at Travis, a flash of electricity darting through her body. This must have been what Ben Franklin experienced with his kite, she thought, trying to laugh it off in her own mind. Maybe she had let *Paris Cassidy, Man with a Gun* get to her and fallen under the spell of his electrifying television alter ego, she told herself.

"No harm done," she said easily, moving back. "I'm forgetting my manners." She glanced at the tree. "I'll be right back, Ben." She turned to follow Travis into the tiny kitchen. "The glasses are in here," she said, reaching up to open an overhead cabinet. "And the scotch," she continued, turning quickly and whirling right into him again, "is . . . right . . . over . . . here. . . ."

He had grabbed her shoulders to steady her, feeling a little overwhelmed himself. He had never been in the company of a female tornado before. For one very strange moment he experienced an urge to shut her mouth by means other than cryptic words.

He's going to kiss me, C.J. thought. Her knees became soft at the thought. What's the matter with me? He's my employer. How am I going to get him into shape if I let myself get involved with him?

C.J. retreated a step, her back now flush against the refrigerator. "The scotch," she repeated, her throat feeling somewhat dry, "is down there." She pointed to a lower cabinet on the opposite side of the room. And then she took away the glass he had just gotten down and poured water into it.

"I changed my mind about the water—" Travis began to repeat, only to see her drinking out of the glass herself. Her cheeks looked a little flushed, and this made him smile. She looked like a young girl with her cheeks pink from some sort of physical exertion.

"Sorry. I'll get you another," she muttered, suddenly realizing what she had done. The dryness in her throat had escalated into an unsurmountable lump, and she'd had to do something about it before she could go on.

Regaining her normal exuberance, she got another glass and then opened the refrigerator. "Damn."

"Another dead plant?" Travis guessed, peering over her shoulder.

C.J. turned and found herself in the very same position again. If he were the suspicious sort, she thought, he'd probably think she was orchestrating this.

"You're going to have to get a bigger kitchen, Clem," he said mildly, smiling down into her face.

He had a very nice smile, she thought. Millions of women *were* right. "At least my kitchen," she said in defense, "has more room in it than your car."

"Not much."

She let the absurd line of conversation drop, and gathered her senses. "I'm afraid I don't have any ice cubes," she told him. "I forgot. The refrigerator's unplugged."

"Doesn't matter, I think I'm going to need it straight," he commented. He got the scotch out of its cupboard and poured two fingers' worth into a glass. "Join me?" he offered.

"No, thank you," she replied. My mind's confused enough as it is, thanks, she added silently. She filled another glass with water and went back to her dying tree. "I think it's beyond hope," she told Travis, examining the leaves slowly. "Serves me right for trusting that freckled face." She saw confusion re-enter Travis's eyes.

He had a feeling that confusion was going to be the natural state of affairs around C.J.

"I usually have Mrs. Odetts look after Ben." She cast an apologetic look toward the tree. Travis got the distinct impression that she did regard it as a person.

"I've had him for years. My Dad gave him to me when I left home."

Probably by popular demand, Travis thought sarcastically.

"Where's home?" he asked, curious.

"Montana."

His eyes narrowed. "Where in Montana?"

C.J. began picking up the ring of brown leaves that circled the pot. They cracked in her fingers. "A little place called Chelsey. Very, very little. Population four hundred, if you include the horses." She smiled fondly as she said it.

"I'm from Montana," he said. He wondered if she was telling the truth. It wouldn't be the first time someone had tried to get close to him by making things up.

"Yes, I know." She dumped the leaves into the trash. "Butte."

Travis took another sip of scotch, then set the glass down on the counter. It was getting late, and he had a lot of things to see to before tomorrow. "It's probably safe to go down now. My fans don't have the greatest staying power." He grinned appreciatively. "I'd better leave you to your ailing friend." Travis nodded toward the denuded tree.

They hadn't gotten anything settled, but she decided that maybe she should let things rest for now. "I'll let you know when I'm holding the funeral," she quipped, a sad smile curving her lips as she looked at the forlorn tree. "See you tomorrow."

She walked him to the door and waved, then went back to tend to the tree and unpack.

It occurred to Travis, as he ducked quickly back into his car under the doorman's worshipful eye, that they hadn't done any talking. It also occurred to him that she hadn't been the least bit impressed with him.

"This might prove to be interesting at that, Clem," he said as he pulled away from the curb. He smiled to himself as he switched on the radio. "Very interesting, indeed."

Three

Travis never bothered setting his alarm clock. He trusted his own internal clock to get him up for his early morning calls at the studio. It rarely failed.

Monday morning, it failed.

He had been up all night, wrestling with both the next week's shooting script, which in his opinion fell excruciatingly short of the mark, and with some of his own paperwork. He knew of many stars, far less in demand than he happened to be at the moment, who had business managers, personal managers, live-in secretaries, investment counselors, publicists and enough people on their payroll to start their own small town. He, on the other hand, felt that he was giving up a piece of himself each time he hired someone to take over another aspect of his life. An agent was a necessary go-between. He didn't have the time to field every single property out there, although Berenstein was doing rather a lamentable job of late, he thought.

And he had given in to Peter's insistence that he take on a publicist. It wasn't in his nature to try to convince magazines to run stories on him. In the beginning Curt Martin had gotten a few crumbs tossed his way, and that had soured Travis on the integrity of magazines in general. He had seen them turn his rather uneventful interviews into articles with titles like: "What I Want My Woman to Sleep In." He was about to let Curt go, when the show took off and suddenly *real* magazines began calling, *asking* to do features on him. Curt no longer needed to call around, pleading for interviews. Now the shoe was on the other foot, and Travis was in a position to turn things down if he so chose.

He wished he were in a position to turn C.J. down. But there were just too many details for him to cope with. As he'd sat, nursing a lone chilled glass of wine, he'd thought about the woman who had suddenly invaded his life. Under normal circumstances, he admitted to himself, he would have wanted to get to know her better. She was attractive, alive—maybe *too* alive—and had a sense of humor and the most beautiful eyes he had ever seen. And her lower jaw didn't grow slack when she looked at him. That was a very important point in her favor. She also didn't look at him as a possible ticket to fame and fortune. Another plus.

The minuses, though, multiplied when she opened her mouth. When he had finally agreed to Peter's suggestion, he'd expected that a personal manager would take over the minor details and keep in the background. Become, in effect, a helpful shadow. C.J. had absolutely no shadowlike qualities. She had the makings of a very domineering woman, no matter how soft she felt against him or how sad her eyes became while she was lamenting the fate of an unwatered tree. Complicating the situation, he would have had trouble accepting a personal manager had she been a bowing and scraping lackey. Independence was something he treasured in himself, not in someone who came to work for him. He was concerned about this new relationship. He was certain that there would be a problem. Maybe lots of them. Their personalities were on a collision course. It was only a matter of time.

Her appearance in his life—actually, "invasion" was a better word for it—had prompted him to stay up half the night. He'd been trying one last time to put his life in order, to prove to himself that he really didn't need her. The hopelessness of the task had overwhelmed him. He realized that he couldn't even make a dent in his fan mail, much less get his woefully out of date appointment book straightened out.

He was surrounded by reminders of his inefficiency. In the corner of the living room was an unopened sack of mail. Fan letters. When he had started out, he had promised himself to answer every one. Then it had been only the more interesting ones. Now he didn't even have time to open the letters, much less try to answer them.

"I suppose I'll need a secretary next. Where does it end?" he'd asked the distorted reflection in his wine-glass.

He knew the answer to that. It didn't. But he wasn't going to give up his independence without a fight.

He'd dragged himself to bed at two, feeling like a prize fighter down for the count.

At five-forty-five the next morning a bell sounded, signaling the next round.

Bell?

The question and the sound filtered through his groggy brain at the same time.

The doorbell. It was his doorbell. The bell went on chiming as he picked up his clock. God, five-forty-five already? he thought, running his hand through his tousled hair. He had just laid his head down a minute ago.

"Well, all right, maybe two," he amended, dragging his body upright. He stumbled to the door. "Damn bell needs a silencer," he muttered under his breath. "Who is it?" he asked through the door.

"C.J."

"C.J.?" he asked, momentarily confused. Then it all returned to him—Peter, the feisty hurricane, the dying benjamina, everything. "Oh, that's right, the haircut enthusiast." He opened the door. "C'mon in, Clem." He gestured toward the living room. "Don't mind the mess. Just trying to pull myself together for you."

C.J. flashed him a patient smile that froze ever so slightly on her lips as she looked at him. All Travis was wearing was a frayed pair of shorts. The frayed ends highlighted exceedingly muscular legs, and the shorts hung low, catching on his hips, bypassing his taut belly and whistle-thin waist. Seeing him like that on the screen was one thing, but seeing Travis in all his sculpted glory a scant five inches away from her was another matter. It rattled her composure.

"You're going to the studio like that?" she asked, reminding herself that lascivious thoughts about her client weren't ethical.

"Are you going to institute a dress code for me?" he asked as he closed the door behind her. His eyes swept over her. She looked far more casual today. The jeans she wore displayed very pleasing curves. She had an excellent shape—for a platoon sergeant.

"No, no dress code." Was he always going to be sarcastic? "I just thought you wanted to avoid getting mobbed. Walk around like that—" she averted her eyes and pretended to look at his living room "—and you're going to wind up being a trophy on someone's mantel before you even get to your car."

"As a matter of fact, you got me out of bed."

C.J. glanced down at her watch. "Oh, I'm sorry," she apologized. Had she gotten her information wrong? Wasn't he on call early?

Travis clutched his heart. "An apology. Wait, let me sit down." He deposited his long frame on the arm of the sofa. "This is your first, I presume?" He eyed her playfully.

"We'll get along a lot better without sarcasm." Unconsciously she started to clean up the coffee table, arranging the scattered papers into neat piles.

He took the papers from her hands and put them down again. "You're my personal manager, not my housekeeper."

She smiled serenely. "I know my job, thank you."

Give me strength, he pleaded silently.

Continuing like this would accomplish nothing, he thought. She would just have to be shown who was boss, that was all. Or fired.

"As a matter of fact," he told her, "I sleep in these."

"Better not let your fans know," she told him. She noticed a section that was torn particularly high on his thigh and looked away. "They'll scale the walls faster than you can say *Paris Cassidy, Man with a Gun*."

She glanced around. Despite the clutter, the room was warm and comfortable. She wondered if it reflected the man behind the barbed tongue. Probably. He certainly didn't strike her as the type to hire an interior decorator. Warm and comfortable, eh? This was going to be worth it, she told herself.

C.J. turned abruptly, and caught him watching her rather intensely. What was going on behind those incredible blue eyes? she wondered. "I thought your studio day started at six-thirty," she said. It was an effort to keep her mind on her work. She had to remember that this incredible specimen, no matter how ill-tempered, was her client.

"It does."

"Then you overslept," she surmised. "I'm glad I decided to show up early. I figured I could go to the studio with you and you could fill me in between scenes. Good thing, huh?"

"That," he informed her, "is a matter of opinion." He watched her move around the room. "Looking for something?"

"Just getting my bearings," she said.

He felt as if he were being staked out. "Look, I still have to get ready," he began. He was going to tell her to go on to the studio and wait for him, but he never got that far.

"Fine, I can wait." She picked up the script he had left on the coffee table and flipped through it, scanning it absently. She had a habit of trying to absorb everything for possible future use. "Did you have a chance to make up that list for me?"

"No," he retorted, annoyed at his failure, and at her for bringing it up. "I haven't had time—"

"My, you're grumpy in the morning. Had your coffee yet? No, of course not," she said in answer to her own question before he had a chance to open his mouth. "You said you just got out of bed. I'll make it for you," she offered cheerfully. "Just show me to the kitchen."

I'd rather show you to the door, he thought. Instead he stoically led her through the living room to the kitchen.

C.J. followed him and tried to keep her eyes on his shoulders, but they kept slipping down to his hips, where the shorts clung provocatively. Yup, his fans would definitely scale fences for this. Lucky thing for him she wasn't a starstruck fan, she thought, forcing her eyes away from the tempting sight before her thoughts got any warmer.

"Here's the kitchen."

C.J. looked around the huge sunlit area. Three of her kitchens could have fit in here, with room to spare.

"I figured that out on my own."

He gave her an enigmatic smile. "I can see why your ex-clients say you're so sharp."

She let his remark pass. "Now if you'll point me to where you keep your coffee, I'll make you a strong cup. A *very* strong cup." There was no mistaking her implication.

He remained in the doorway and simply pointed to the pantry to her left. Wordlessly C.J. opened the pantry doors and searched for a moment before she came to an unopened can of coffee. "Drip?"

"I beg your pardon?"

"How do you prepare your coffee? Percolator? Drip?" she asked, turning the can around to find a clue.

He pointed to a coffee maker obscured by a large bread box.

"Thank you. I'll have everything ready for you by the time you're dressed," she promised, then turned her attention to the job at hand.

For a moment he remained where he was, quietly studying her. He wondered if she knew how good those jeans made her look from behind.

She turned from the coffee machine toward the sink and was surprised to see him still standing there, staring at her. She felt as if he were appraising her physically, which generated diametrically opposed feelings. She was at once annoyed and pleased.

"I thought women employees balked at making coffee for their bosses these days." He purposely emphasized the word "bosses."

He was trying to get under her skin, she thought. Nice try, but no dice. "I'm far too secure a person to feel threatened by a cup of coffee. Besides," she added brightly, "I'm making myself a cup, too."

"Make yourself at home," he commented. "Although I'm sure you will, no matter what I say."

Her smile told him that he was right. "Thank you." She looked at him expectantly, then glanced at her watch.

Irritated, he retreated.

This situation was going to be impossible, he told himself, stepping into the shower. The woman was annoying, smug and a know-it-all. What made things worse was that she acted as if she were competence personified.

And she probably was, damn her.

As he stood in the shower, surrounded by a cloud of steam, he began enumerating all the reasons he hadn't wanted her around. He lathered himself ferociously. She was a woman, and women had already invaded his life farther than he cared to let them. He was grateful to his fans, but they were also the reason he felt so trapped these days. They indirectly dictated the kind of roles he could get. If he changed, they could withdraw their favor at any time, and he would be left out in the cold. But he could very well end up there anyway, if his fans whimsically chose someone else to bestow their favors on next season. Damned if he did, damned if he didn't.

He simply couldn't see himself getting along with a woman who was so involved in his life.

Especially, he thought, recalling Peter's testimonial, a competent woman. The last thing he needed when he felt control slipping away was a woman who thrived on taking over. It made the macho man of the year, *him*, feel inadequate, threatened. And he didn't like feeling threatened.

Besides, he thought, angling his body to catch the needlelike spray, she was too damn attractive to make this thing work. Last night, when they had inadvertently brushed up against each other in her tiny kitchen, he had responded to her. Something inside him had stirred. It had surprised him. He hadn't felt that way in quite a while.

He argued with himself that it was because he had been keeping women at arm's length lately. He felt that any woman who became too friendly had an ulterior motive. Was it Travis McQuade or Paris Cassidy they were interested in?

With C.J. he knew what she was after. She wanted to rearrange his life according to some vast eternal plan she kept locked up in her head. Well, it might work for the likes of Baxter Tremayne, but he was different.

For one thing, he wasn't the publicity-seeking creature her past employers had been, he thought, reaching for a towel. For another, he—

"Oh, damn," he swore. He had forgotten to put out the towels again. He was forgetting to do a lot of things lately. He supposed he'd have to get a housekeeper next.

No, the idea of having another woman around, poking through his private possessions, rankled him. It was almost as bad as having someone invading his mind, the way C.J. threatened to do.

There was that word again. *Threatened.*

"And meanwhile, you're standing in a steam-covered shower, drip-drying." Annoyed with himself, he kicked open the shower door and went out to the linen closet for a towel.

Hearing the commotion, C.J. thought he was through with his shower. She poked her head out into the hallway. "Travis, you're—"

His head turned in her direction.

Oh, no! she thought, quickly ducking her head back. You're naked, that's what you are.

Okay, bright girl, how are you going to handle this one? Coming on Andrea Addams in the nude was one thing. Her last employer had come in from swimming nude in her pool and acted as if it were the most natural thing in the world to parade around her living room wearing only a scarlet ribbon in her hair, but C.J. wasn't sure how Travis was going to react to this unexpected screening.

She took a deep breath and tried to select her best tack. All she had meant to do was tell him that he was out of milk. She knew he liked his coffee light. She knew a lot of things about him. That was her job. To know her clients inside and out.

But not this well.

How did one casually brush off accidentally seeing what could very possibly be God's most gorgeous creation? Bodies like that were very, very rare. If he never even opened his mouth, C.J. could see why he had the following he did.

She struggled to regain control by forcing her attention back to the French toast she'd decided to make.

She felt like Clemmie Parker again, not the competent C.J. she had worked so hard to become. One glance at that man's physique and she had turned into mush. She should be ashamed of herself. She had come a long way, worked hard at smoothing the rough edges that had marked her earlier life. A sophisticated woman would easily laugh off a mishap like this one. Or take advantage of it, she couldn't help thinking.

She could do neither.

Act as if it didn't happen, she told herself. That would be the best way to handle it, she decided. Pretend it hadn't happened. She reached for the orange juice. Only her racing pulse knew differently.

"Clem, I'm afraid this isn't going to work," Travis said, walking into the room.

She turned toward him, hoping that she looked sufficiently composed. "Not if you keep calling me 'Clem.' I prefer 'C.J.'"

"And I prefer to be—what's that?"

C.J. smiled. A temporary stay of execution. "French toast."

"My favorite." He looked at her incredulously. Unlike most popular idols, Travis had never listed his favorite things for the movie star magazines. What he owed to his public was the best possible performance he could render, not how large his biceps were, or what he liked to eat for breakfast. How had she found out?

"I know," C.J. said, sliding the slices onto a plate and covering them with syrup. She placed the plate on the table, saying, "You'll have to take your coffee black. I was coming to tell you that you're out of milk." She cringed, realizing that she had slipped. Terrific way of ignoring the situation, C.J. Congratulations.

To her relief he let the comment pass. Apparently he didn't want to discuss what had just occurred in his hallway any more than she did. "You know I like milk in my coffee." There was wonder in his voice.

"And that blue is your favorite color." She seated herself comfortably next to him, cradling her coffee cup in her hands. "I believe in doing my homework." She smiled, hoping he'd forget the incident in the hall. "I know where your favorite restaurants are, that you hate breakfast cereal and where your birthmark is."

"You got that first hand."

He looked amused. C.J. looked down at the tablecloth. "Sorry about that. I thought you were through."

She looked cute when she was flustered, he thought. "I forgot to put out towels."

C.J. looked up. "You need a housekeeper."

She was starting in again. He couldn't believe it. "Clem, what I need is a person who'll listen when I talk, not talk for me. Understood?"

She nodded. "Understood."

And undoubtedly disregarded, he added silently.

C.J. took a sip of her coffee. "Does that mean you've decided to keep me on?"

So she knew how close she'd come to being fired, did she? Maybe she was clairvoyant, after all, he thought. "I figure we'll work on it. Besides—" he took another bite of his breakfast "—you make terrific French toast."

"I make a lot of terrific things," she told him with neither false pride nor false modesty. It was just a fact.

"I bet you do," he said, and she wasn't quite sure how to take that. Well, no matter, she'd figure him out before long. Until then, she had a lot of work ahead of her. Peter had said his affairs were hopeless.

C.J. mentally rolled up her sleeves and prepared to dig in. "Do you have an address book?" she asked as he finished eating.

"Yes, in the den. Why?"

She was already on her feet. "I thought I'd make my own list so I can get started."

He shook his head as he followed her out. He watched her look around the cluttered room. "Lady, take it from me, you've already gotten started."

She looked at him expectantly. "I don't want to add to this mess. Could you give me a small hint?"

"I could." He stood right where he was, leaning rakishly against the doorway, his arms crossed in front of his chest.

C.J. pressed her lips together. "Would you?"

He laughed, uncrossing his arms. "Okay, here." He dug under one pile. His smile faded. The book wasn't there. It was C.J.'s turn to smile.

"Well, it was here somewhere," he muttered.

"About that housekeeper..." C.J. began.

He found the book and slapped it into her hand. "Let her find her own address book. I'm late."

C.J. walked behind him as they went to the front door. She looked over the names that were scribbled on the pages. "You have horrid handwriting."

"So my teachers all told me."

"Where would I find your hairdresser?" She stepped out of the way just in time as he shut the front door behind her.

"In his shop."

"Very funny. Don't think I've forgotten our discussion about your hair."

"Leave my hair to me. What are you doing?" he asked as she opened the passenger door of his car.

"I thought we'd go in together."

"Don't I have a say in this?"

"Of course you do."

He kept his say to himself. "Oh, all right, get in." He started the car.

This was probably the way the Indians felt when the Pilgrims invaded, he thought as he drove away.

Four

———

They arrived on the set half an hour late.

"Hey, Travis is here!"

C.J. turned to see a heavyset older man walking toward them. She recognized Grant Goodale, Travis's co-star in the series. Some twenty years ago Grant had been the handsome young leading man, playing the type of role Travis now had. He had left his hit series in an attempt to parlay his television success into a big movie career. The gamble had failed, and his hoped-for career had never materialized.

C.J. thought that a man who had played his ace and lost would be somewhat bitter. Especially about playing second banana to a man wearing the crown he had once worn himself. But the greeting Grant had shouted seemed genuine and warm, as did his manner.

"I was beginning to get worried," Grant told him. "You're usually the first one on the set." Then he noticed C.J., and a large grin spread across his face. "Oh, I see." He gave C.J. the most thorough ten-second going-over she had ever received. But she couldn't take offense. The look in his eyes was more appreciative than anything. A leer would have bothered her. This was more a compliment.

"No, you don't see," Travis said to Grant. C.J. detected a trace of affection in his voice, but it was plainly directed at Grant, not at her.

Now what made me think of that? she asked herself. Why in heaven's name should the man feel any affection for his personal manager? The thought had come out of left field, but its mere existence bothered her.

She was so caught up in her thoughts that she didn't realize Travis was introducing her to Grant. "This is my personal manager. C.J. Parker."

Grant smiled broadly, his grin raising his wide cheeks. He made C.J. think of an old, friendly hound. "Well, if you're what personal managers look like these days, I think I'll look into finding one of my own." He stuck out his large hand. "Hi, I'm Grant Goodale."

C.J. shook his hand. "Yes, I know."

"She says that a lot," Travis interjected. C.J. didn't find his tone entirely pleasant.

C.J. smiled, disregarding Travis. She had a feeling she was going to like Grant. His eyes were warm.

"I've got to get to makeup," Travis told her. "Grant'll show you to my trailer."

She watched Travis walk away. He was the recipient of cheerful greetings from the cast and crew as he made his way to the makeup department. She was struck by the camaraderie he seemed to share with everyone.

"Everyone likes him, don't they?" she asked Grant.

"Who? Travis? Why sure, he's the salt of the earth, as they used to say in my day."

His day hadn't been all that long ago, C.J. thought. Why didn't he sound as if he envied this new man on the scene? Most men finding themselves in his position would have, yet she couldn't detect any jealousy in his voice. Instead he seemed fond of Travis. Maybe he was just relieved to be working again, she decided.

"Easiest man there is to work with," Grant told her.

I don't know about that, she thought.

"And believe me," Grant went on, "I ought to know. I worked with some doozies." He jerked his thumb at his thick chest. "Yours truly not withstanding," he chuckled. It was a deep guttural chuckle that came rumbling up from his rather expansive waistline.

So this is what hunks become when they're put out to pasture, she thought.

"C'mon." Grant took her arm. "Let me take you to his dressing room."

She wanted to get to know Travis's surroundings. It might help her unravel the enigma he represented. If she understood him, she would find him easier to work with. Maybe. "No, thanks," she said quickly.

Her answer surprised Grant, and he looked at her quizzically. "But Travis said . . ."

"I know what Travis said, but I'd rather stick around the set, get the feel of things. Don't worry," she said, seeing a dubious look sweeping across his face, "I'll stay out of the way. This isn't my first time on a set." She looked around. They were standing in the middle of Paris Cassidy's office. "I want to see him act."

Grant could accept that. He was used to starstruck fans trying to get on the set to see Travis play Paris. This one had a free pass. Why shouldn't she want to take advantage of it?

"There's none better," he assured her. "Here, you can sit here." He pointed to a canvas-back chair with his name on it. "Travis knows his lines and doesn't take your head off if you don't know yours. Never met anyone who had more of a right to be conceited and wasn't."

He was laying it on a bit thick, C.J. thought. Maybe it *was* to cover resentfulness. She wondered if her original assessment had been wrong.

C.J. accepted the seat he offered her. "Thank you," she said as she sat down. "That's rather high praise coming from the star of *Malibu Detective*."

At the mention of his late, lamented series, Grant beamed sheepishly. She half expected him to kick the dust and mutter, "Ah, shucks."

"I think I'm going to like you, honey."

Good. I'm going to need all the help I can get, C.J. thought. She settled back in the chair. "Tell me about Travis."

Grant looked at her thoughtfully for a moment as the camera crew began setting up, increasing the noise

level around them. He pulled up another chair and
straddled it, then leaned forward and spoke in an almost conspiratorial tone. "You sure you're his personal manager and not some reporter?"

"I'm sure. I just want to get to know as much as I
can about him in order to do my job." I need to get
inside the man's skin, she added silently. "I take it,"
she said as a sound boom was pushed past her, "by
your tone that he doesn't care much for reporters."

Grant laughed. It was a big, booming laugh that
didn't go unnoticed by the people closest to them.
"You got that right, honey. They're always going for
some dirt, or turning his words inside out." C.J.
thought that Grant sounded almost protective as he
spoke. "I guess they all figure that maybe he's too
good to be true," Grant told her. "Maybe he is at
that."

C.J.'s interest was definitely piqued. "Oh?"

Her tone was leading, and Grant needed no more
coaxing. "He dried me out."

C.J. said nothing, but the look on her face encour-
aged Grant to go on. The friendly voice turned serious. As she listened, she could see that her first
impression had been right. What Grant felt for Travis
was not the false, superficial friendship that the stu-
dios liked to promote for the benefit of the public.
Grant really cared about his co-star.

"You remembered the name of my series. Most
people, if they remember me at all, remember that.
And only that. Not much else to recall over the past
twenty years. Some forgettable projects." His voice
grew distant, as if he were trying to put space between

himself and his words. "A lot of forgettable years that piled painfully on top of one another." He scratched his salt-and-pepper beard self-consciously. "God knows I tried to forget them. One bottle at a time. Don't know why I got a chance on this series. I think the producer cut his teeth on *Malibu Detective*." He laughed disparagingly. "But after the initial shock wore off, I found myself falling back on my old habits. I needed courage to show up every morning, courage to face this handsome new guy they'd put in the lead without hating his guts. Bottled courage."

He grew silent for a moment. "Travis caught on right away. We went out drinking one night soon after the show started. Well, I went out drinking," Grant clarified. "He just kind of came along and sipped." He chuckled, shaking his head as he remembered. "And somewhere during the evening, he told me I wasn't going to do that anymore. That I wasn't going to ruin the rest of my life the way I had the past twenty years. I was pretty belligerent at the time, and I asked him who was going to stop me. He said very quietly that *he* would." Grant paused, letting the words sink in.

Amid the din of a set coming to life, C.J. heard nothing but the silent message in Grant's story. It was evident that he felt Travis really cared about what happened to him. And that he cared about Travis.

"Haven't had a drink since then," he told her with pride. "Travis is a real good guy."

"Yes," C.J. said slowly, "I'm beginning to see that."

Grant's earlier words of praise about Travis's professionalism had not been just idle chatter. He was letter perfect the first time through, C.J. noted. Better than the part called for. And when the guest star of the week flubbed her lines three times and irritably retreated to her dressing room, Travis kept his temper, joking with Grant and several others on the set.

It was only when he spotted her that his expression changed. It tightened, C.J. thought. That was the only way to describe it. He looked like a tiger watching a potential enemy approach.

Was she the enemy? Why, for heaven's sake? When everyone around him was swearing to his geniality, why did he want to play Saint George and the dragon, with her as the dragon? Well, whether he liked her or not, she had a job to do. Once she took on an assignment, she saw it through. Having allowed herself a few hours to watch him interact with other people, she decided that it was time to get to work herself.

He saw her walk off the set out of the corner of his eye. Except when he was in front of the camera, he had been aware of her all morning. What was she up to? Why was she just watching him like that, as if she were studying him? He realized that he kept thinking of her as an opponent, someone to be wary of. Well, maybe she was exactly that. She looked as if she enjoyed getting her way too much.

You're overreacting, he cautioned himself. She's just here to get you organized.

But damn it, he shouldn't *need* anyone to help him get organized. This was his life. He should be able to take care of it himself. What kind of a man had other people doing everything for him? He didn't believe in self-indulgence. That was the mark of decay. And Travis meant to stay around for a long, long time.

"Hey, Travis, lighten up," Grant coaxed. The hamlike hands grabbed the muscles on either side of Travis's neck and began to massage. Travis was two inches taller, and Grant had to reach for a vantage point. "You're as tense as a bride on her wedding day."

Travis laughed softly. The remark sounded typical of Grant. "Brides aren't tense anymore, Grant."

Grant shrugged good-naturedly. "What do I know? It's been a while since I had one. Figure six is enough, don't you?"

"One is all I want," Travis answered, still thinking about C.J.

"And when's that one gonna be?" Grant asked. Before Travis had a chance to say anything, Grant laughed out loud at his own question. "Hey, what am I saying? With all those young, breathless ladies out there waiting for just a glimpse of you, you don't ever have to get married. You can have it all."

Travis smiled, humoring Grant, knowing that it was his own past he was reliving. Travis wasn't interested in the bevy of women who stalked him. He thought of the fan letters. They weren't after him. They were after Paris Cassidy. Travis wanted someone who'd love an ex-cowhand from Montana, not a star.

Travis and C.J. maintained what amounted to an armed truce for the first two weeks. He wasn't exactly thrilled about having her around, but he was beginning to accept her part in his daily life. He even, he thought at times, looked forward to seeing her. Even at her worst, and he thought there were plenty of "worsts," there was something beguiling about her. There were even times when he thought he might have been interested in her personally, if only she wouldn't act like some angel of mercy who'd been sent to straighten out his life.

Women couldn't straighten out his life. They were responsible for the mess it was in, for the career stagnation he was experiencing. And all the while they were there, demanding a piece of him, demanding payment for having put him where he was, where he really didn't want to be—on a pedestal made of papier-mâché.

And C.J. was as demanding as the rest, even if in a different way. She seemed intent on getting into every nook and cranny of his life, digging in like a determined gopher whose very existence depended on the path she was forging.

Pushy. That was the word for her. Damn pushy.

There was also another word for her, he thought as he remembered his reaction to her that first evening in her kitchen. That word was *attractive*.

But her being attractive did not erase the fact that she was encroaching on his life at a phenomenal pace with her elaborate schedules. He grudgingly had to admit that he no longer felt overwhelmed by petty details. But the very fact that things were running so much smoother, that she could juggle the details of his life when he couldn't, made him resent her.

It was illogical. By nature he wasn't an illogical creature. He was very logical. And easygoing. But when it came to C.J., he found himself fighting her every step of the way, battling both her and his own conflicting feelings at the same time.

And yet all the while he silently applauded her ability to stay toe to toe with him.

Maybe he was going crazy, he thought, stretching out in his trailer during his morning break. He began to go through a series of exercises that he used to keep himself in shape. And sane.

He wasn't going crazy, he told himself. She just had an uncanny ability to rub him the wrong way. No, that wasn't fair. It wasn't C.J. who rubbed him the wrong way. It was the way she did things. She did them well. And the better she did them, the worse the situation became.

He stopped stretching and ran his hand through his hair in frustration. God, there certainly was a lot to run through these days. He made a mental note to call Andretti later and make an appointment. No, he amended, he'd let Clem make the appointment. That should make her happy. He had to stop feeling so defensive about everything.

What was wrong with him? He was faulting her for doing the job he was paying her to do. That would be like being irritated at his agent for getting him the plumb role of the year.

Fat chance of that, Travis thought sarcastically, glancing at the script that had been on his dressing table for the past three days. Berenstein had been trying to talk him into signing for the role for weeks now.

They were scheduled to shoot during the series' spring hiatus. So far he had held out, hoping for something better to come along. But he knew the odds of that were small.

Walker! was another one of those hero-against-the-odds, hero-gets-lush-women, hero-wins movies. No real substance, no real plot, no real acting required. He could phone his performance in along with an eight-by-ten glossy, preferably barechested, he thought ruefully. From what little he had seen of the script, his chest would get more exposure than his talent would.

How the hell was he going to establish his career when all he had to work with were weak, mindless roles with no more substance to them than cotton candy? It was meat and potatoes that fed you, not fluff. When would he get someone to take him seriously?

Maybe that was why he was fighting Clem so hard, he thought. Subconsciously he felt that she was more successful in her field than he was in his. She was so professional. She had worked with the best. How could she help but look down on what he was doing? She was intelligent enough to realize that there was no depth to the role he played. And there might never be. He might be stuck being Paris Cassidy, or some facsimile, until the end of his career.

Which could come shortly.

There was a knock on the door. He got up from the cot and grabbed a towel to wipe the perspiration from his face. He was going to require a touch-up from makeup, he thought. "C'mon in—the door's open."

To his surprise, Andretti walked in, followed by C.J.

"I hope you realize how much this is costing me, Travis," Andretti said in his trembling contralto. Andretti always sounded as if everything around him was in turmoil. "I don't do plebian things like make house calls. But when I got her call, it sounded like a positive emergency." He cocked his head from side to side quickly, like a blue jay undecided about which end of the worm to attack first. "I see she wasn't exaggerating." He clucked under his breath, pursing his lips critically. He put down his oversized travel bag and pulled out a large dark blue cloth, which he promptly draped around Travis's costume. "I feel like I'm the U.S. Cavalry bailing out Custer." He lifted a strand of chestnut hair. "Except Custer's hair was shorter."

Andretti didn't believe in beginnings, middles or ends. His mind was always working at a frantic pace, so he generally just leaped into the middle of a conversation, leaving it to the listener to sort things out.

What Travis sorted out, he didn't like. "What the hell are you doing here?" he asked.

Andretti took out his scissors. "My, you were right," he said to C.J. "He *is* waspish about this." He looked down his long nose at Travis. "For your information, I'm saving my reputation, just as she said. The studio may let you do what you want, but you're one of my clients, and I can't have you walking around as if you're the lead in *Lassie Come Home*."

C.J. could see the dark look in Travis's eyes as he glared at her in the mirror. Too bad. He had put off getting this hair cut and she was just doing him a favor, she told herself.

Undaunted by his scowl, she retreated to the latest sack of mail. She had decided to separate the scores of letters into two piles—those that deserved some sort of answer, and those that merited only a photograph with his signature stamped across the bottom. Digging in, she began sorting.

Today's batch consisted mostly of mash letters. Those went into the picture pile. The few that appeared to be intelligently written she set aside. She would go through those later and pick the best for him to read. He had balked at that originally even though he knew she was right. He had wanted to look at them all, but lack of time made that impossible, and he ended up feeling too guilty to look at any of them. What Travis insisted on was that each letter be answered in some form or another. She was going to have to see about getting a few reliable people to handle that. She didn't look forward to mentioning it to him. He had been bearish about all her suggestions. None of her clients had ever been so hard to work with.

Travis watched her go through the letters, sorting them almost as quickly as she took them out of their envelopes. He thought of how long it had taken him. She probably counted speed reading as one of her talents, as well.

"Voilá!" Andretti declared with no attempt at humility as he removed the cloth from around Travis's neck. "You're a man again instead of a werewolf. And I—" he looked at his watch "—am running late. I hope the gods have seen fit to leave my shop intact. I left Jack and Gordon in charge." He sighed dramatically. "Good help is soooo hard to find these days."

"Tell me about it," Travis said, looking directly at C.J.

Now what's wrong with him? she grumped silently.

"Next time, don't wait so long to call me," Andretti admonished as he walked out.

"Next time, wait until I do call you," Travis countered.

"I thought I did," Andretti said, confused.

Travis shook his head. "Never mind. I'll explain some other time."

"Show people," Andretti muttered to himself rather audibly as he closed the door behind him.

Travis turned to C.J. "Why didn't you consult me?"

"I did," she said mildly, putting down the letters. "I told you two weeks ago that you needed a haircut."

"Stating your opinion in passing is not the same thing as consulting me." He could feel his temper beginning to erupt.

He was being petty and ridiculous, she decided. "I can't come running to you with every single thing I think of. What's the point of having a manager if I have to come with my hat in my hand every time I want to make a move? I owe you the benefit of my judgment."

"You owe me obedience."

That just about tore it. C.J. got up, feeling as if she had come to the end of her rope. She was tempted to hang him with it. "If you want obedience," she said between clenched teeth, "get a puppy. I'm your personal manager! In case you haven't noticed, the root of that word is 'manage.'" She raised herself up on her toes in order to yell at him.

"That doesn't mean you own me!" he shouted back.

"Own you? I don't want to own you. If I owned you, you ill-tempered ex-cowboy, I would have sold you a long time ago!" She took a deep breath, trying to control what was left of her temper. "Look, if you want to go around looking like a sheep dog from now on, that's your business. It's *all* your business." She dug down into her purse and pulled out his address book. "Here!" She threw it on the table. "Go find somebody else's head to bite off!"

And with that she stormed out.

She had never quit before, though there had been times when she had been sorely tempted to. Some of the people she had worked with had needed to be coddled before anything could be done with them or the atrocious state of their affairs. She had dealt with temperamental people before. What had come over her?

But it wasn't just temperament with Travis. There was something more, something else behind the way he reacted to her. It was as if he resented her for what she was. She hadn't a clue about how to deal with him. The harder she tried, the worse the situation became.

She glanced down at her speedometer and realized that she was doing seventy. Damn him, he was even getting to her in her own car.

C.J. eased her foot from the gas pedal and waited until the speedometer registered fifty-five again. Damn that man, anyway, she thought, slamming her hand against the dashboard.

She was still slamming things several hours later in her apartment. This wasn't doing her or the apartment any good, she thought, catching a vase that had narrowly escaped being broken as she slammed the drawer of her desk. She needed a vacation. She had been all set to take one right after she had given Andrea her resignation in New York. But then Peter's call had come, and the proposition had sounded as though it might be fun.

"Fun," she muttered aloud. "Just like playing Russian roulette is fun."

The man was utterly, totally, horridly impossible. Well, she was glad she was through working for him. It went completely against her grain to give up this way, but it was for the best, she told herself. Working with him was like being with Mr. Hyde while everyone thought you were with Dr. Jekyll.

"Well, I'm glad it's over," she announced to the soufflé she shoved into her microwave. "Glad!"

If you're so glad, why are you shouting at your oven? a little voice inside her mind asked.

The image of his face came to her, followed quickly by the memory of his unexpected dash into the hall for a towel. A hot, tingling sensation shot through her like a miniexplosion.

"Okay," she conceded out loud, "so he's good-looking, but that doesn't alter the fact that he's crazy.

I've got to put that into my contract from now on. I don't work for crazy people, no matter how popular they are.''

The doorbell rang.

"Now what?" she muttered, walking over to the door. Building security had gotten lax lately. Several door to door salesmen had gotten through. She glanced at her watch impatiently. It was kind of late for that, but they were a determined breed, so one never knew.

Heaven help them both if it was one of those now. She was in no mood to be polite.

"Who is it?" she snapped.

"Special delivery."

The voice was deep and gruff. Just the way she felt. "I didn't order anything."

"Somebody did."

She sighed, beginning to walk away. "Leave it at the door." She'd look at it in the morning.

"Can't. You gotta sign for it."

Damn. Who would be delivering things at this late hour? she thought testily. C.J. marched back to the door and swung it open. "Okay, okay, I'll sign for—"

She stopped. There, in front of her, was a big, lush Ficus benjamina in a pot.

And the man holding the pot was Travis.

Five

***

C.J. made no move to let him in. Instead she just stared at him incredulously.

"Can the tree and I come in?"

"The tree can. I don't know about you." She didn't remove her hand from the doorknob. She was wavering. Part of her wanted to let him in, and part of her wanted to slam the door shut once and for all, both literally and figuratively.

What was he doing here?

She could have sworn that he actually looked relieved when she had left the studio. He'd appeared glad to be rid of her. Now he was here, standing in her doorway.

Beware of stars bearing gifts, her little voice chimed in.

"C'mon, Clem," he prodded. "Do you know how hard it is to find a Ficus benjamina at this time of night?"

It was past ten. "I don't know," she answered, still blocking his entrance. "I never tried." She hesitated, confused. He had gotten what he was after, hadn't he? He had goaded her into quitting. So why was he here with a peace offering?

She had to ask. "What are you doing, wandering around Wilshire Boulevard at ten o'clock at night with a tree?"

"Trying to find a way to apologize."

She could see how difficult this was for him. He looked so damn sincere, yet so awkward that she couldn't stand it. C.J. swept open the door. "All right, you found it."

Travis carried the tree into her apartment and made his way to the kitchen. He set the pot down where the old tree had stood. "How's this?"

Was the man finally asking her approval on something? she marveled. Maybe there was hope for him yet.

"Fine." She watched him warily. Why had he really gone through all this trouble? I swear, you are the most impossible man to figure out, she thought.

He stepped away from the tree and tilted his head in an attempt to decide if it looked all right where it was. C.J. noticed that there was a huge red ribbon decorating the pot. He had crushed the bow against his chest while carrying the heavy pot in. She leaned over and touched the bow, as if to assure herself that it was really there. That all this was really happening.

"Thank you." Her throat felt dry again. It was getting to be the general state of affairs when she was around him. "I had no idea they had all-night nurseries in Los Angeles," she said tongue-in-cheek, trying not to let him see how touched she was by his gesture.

Just when she'd thought she had him all figured out...

"They don't," he answered seriously as he dusted himself off. "It took a bit of bribing. Grant's got a friend who does landscaping, and he knew someone who knew someone who was willing to go back to his shop for me."

C.J. nodded, still looking at the tree. It was big and lush, a far cry from her old tree. She stood looking at it for a long, silent moment, then turned to Travis.

"Why'd you do it?" she asked quietly. One leaf had caught on his shirt, and she picked it off. She twirled the stem in her fingertips as she waited for his answer.

"I told you." It was difficult for him to admit that he was wrong. He wondered if she knew just how difficult. "I bought it to apologize," he repeated.

It wasn't enough of an answer. "Why?"

"Clem," he said in exasperation, walking into her living room, "you're not making this easy."

"No," she agreed, "I'm not." She followed him. "But, then, you haven't exactly made the past two weeks a party, either." She studied his face. He was a strange man. He had bitten her head off over a trivial thing like her arranging to get him a much needed haircut, and then he had spent his few precious free hours banging on closed doors, trying to hunt down a tree for her. "I was just doing my job," she insisted.

"I realize that." He looked away.

She wouldn't let him off the hook. She purposely put herself into his line of vision. "Don't you want me to do my job?"

"Yes, of course I do," he said. He had come for absolution, realizing that he had been wrong in treating her the way he had. He had thought she would welcome him in. Instead she appeared wary, uncertain. He knew it shouldn't, but it irritated him. He wished she'd just take the tree and be done with it. "That's what I'm paying you for."

She meandered back to the plant. It was taller than she was. A large card was attached to one of its branches, explaining all about its care and feeding. She removed it carefully, putting it on the counter. Too bad Travis hadn't come with a card, as well, she thought.

C.J. looked down at the leaf she had removed from him. Unconsciously she stroked it. "Does this mean you want me to come back to work? Or is it your quaint way of saying goodbye?"

"I'd like you to come back." The words were muttered quietly.

C.J. wanted to prolong the moment. Not for revenge, but to thrash things out. She could detect his irritation under his contrite surface. If she was going to come back, she wanted things to be different between them. She didn't want to be bought off. His irritation was an indication that perhaps things wouldn't be better. But, then, damn it, why had he come over?

He saw the look on her face. She was hesitating. "Clem, this is damn hard for me," he told her.

She faced the situation with humor. When all else fails, smile, she thought. She grinned. "I know it. I'm savoring it."

She looked like the drawing of a mischievous fairy he had once seen in a storybook. Was he doing the right thing? He wasn't sure. All he knew was that he didn't want her to quit. "Then you'll come back?"

"Sure. You need me."

He felt himself balking at the word. "Well, I wouldn't exactly go that far...."

She nodded at the tree. "You already have. Apology accepted." C.J. smiled again. "Sit down." She indicated the sofa. "Now that I'm back, I have to know something."

Travis sat down and heard water sloshing beneath him. Oh, yeah, the water sofa.

The movement of the water was rather soothing after the long, tiring day he had put in. He leaned back, letting the sofa more or less envelop him, and closed his eyes. "What's your question?"

"Are we still going to go at it like the Hatfields and the McCoys?"

The sofa shifted. He felt her sitting down next to him. "That depends."

"On what?"

He opened his eyes. She was sitting only a few inches from him. He shifted slightly, and C.J. moved toward him involuntarily. Her furniture had definite possibilities, he told himself. She was rather appealing, he thought again as she moved back to her original position. "On how you go about your job," he said, answering her question.

She shook her head. "I'm sorry, but it's not in me to come running to you with every little thing. I don't work that way," she told him firmly.

"How well I've come to know that." But the corners of his mouth had risen in a smile. Was there a truce in the making? she wondered. She sincerely hoped so. She didn't try to explore why she felt that way; it made her too uneasy. She decided to investigate the matter later.

"But it *is* my life you're trying to organize, you know." She was wearing perfume. Somehow, tonight its scent was more intense, more enticing.

More.

The word seemed to fit well with her. She was far more *everything* than any woman he had ever known. The realization had come to him five minutes after she had stormed out of his trailer that afternoon. A strange unrest had ensued when he thought he was rid of her. That, and an emptiness. She had been with him only two weeks, and yet he felt as if she were a part of him. How had she managed that?

"I know." She lowered her voice for emphasis. This time she shifted and he slid toward her. The cushion undulated beneath her thighs, rubbing them in a sensual rhythmic motion that subsided slowly.

How would it feel to have his hands do that to her?

"It's...it's a very nice tree," she said haltingly, feeling suddenly very flustered. What the hell was the matter with her? Was she falling victim to the Travis McQuade syndrome? "I really do appreciate you going out and looking for it."

"It wasn't easy. Nothing about you is easy," he said softly, hypnotized by the expression on her face. The light in the living room was low. One lone hurricane lamp illuminated the entire area. "Do you always sit around in the dark?" he asked.

She shook her head, and her hair fell over her face. He reached out to push it back, tucking it behind her ear.

She sat very still, almost afraid to breathe. What was he doing to her? *Why* was he doing this to her? She felt confusion reigning supreme as something warm and pliant rose within her. She moved back, stunned by the force of her reaction. Perversely, the sofa brought them closer together. She felt his thigh touch hers.

What would it be like to have him hold her, to have him kiss her?

Kiss her? Was she crazy? The man would become utterly impossible to deal with. She had to put a stop to whatever was happening right now, or else she'd never be able to get her job done right. He'd feel as if he had the upper hand and . . . and . . .

Whoa. Since when did this turn into a war? she asked herself. There wasn't supposed to *be* an upper hand. This was supposed to be an equal relationship, not an arm wrestling match.

He had the most beautiful blue eyes she had ever seen. They looked as if God had had an extra piece of sky left over after Creation and had used it for Travis's eyes. They were light, entrancing and thoroughly hypnotic as they held her in place.

Her mind was drifting.

"I...um..." What were they talking about? She had lost the thread somewhere in his eyes.

"Clem?"

He was touching her face again, cupping it between his hands. He was making it exceedingly hard for her to maintain her composure.

"Yes?"

"Do you think you could stop talking for just a minute?"

"Yes, I think so."

"Good." He lowered his head toward hers.

For heaven's sake, stop him, her mind shouted. What do you think you're doing?

Snaring a bit of heaven, maybe? another side of her whispered.

Snaring trouble is more like it.

Trouble came in at twelve o'clock high.

She would have thought, based on his screen image, that Travis McQuade would kiss roughly. The character he portrayed was tough, rough. She realized that actors and their roles were different, but she had so little else to go on. And the Travis McQuade she'd seen over the past few weeks was a man given to cryptic comments and hooded looks. She still didn't really *know* him, even though she prided herself on being a quick judge of character.

His kiss was gentle, soft. It was a surprise.

It was also breathtaking.

He coaxed a response from her. She had no way of knowing that he was almost as surprised as she was at what was happening between them.

When he had come over, tree in hand, he'd had nothing more on his mind than to make amends and ask her back. He had been rude that afternoon. He didn't know if it was the mounting pressures of his series or the frustration he felt over his career that was getting to him, or the fact that she had blithely gone over his head to do something. But in either case, there was no excuse for snapping at her the way he had.

There was something about C.J. that kept him wondering. The problem was, he didn't exactly know what it had him wondering. Or if he did, he wasn't admitting it to himself.

Maybe he already had at that, he thought, as he allowed himself to kiss her. Maybe he knew exactly what it was that he was wondering about her. And *that* worried him.

C.J.'s mind was beginning to slip into a haze. Travis had put his arm around her shoulder and the sofa had done the rest, bringing her practically into his lap. His hands had left her face and were now holding her against him, one hand stroking her back, making her feel as liquid as the sofa beneath her.

The haze burned off, allowing her body to be invaded by a blazing need.

Somewhere in the distance a bell rang.

The end of round one? C.J. thought vaguely.

No, wait, the soufflé. Dinner.

Slowly reality came back to her. With an effort she put her hands against his chest. How could something so rock hard feel so good against her?

"My dinner," she breathed heavily.

"What about it?" He kissed her ear lightly.

"It's calling me," she managed to say. Her stomach was quivering.

He stopped kissing her. "What?"

C.J. pointed toward the kitchen. Actually, she was pointing toward her bedroom. He had gotten her so disoriented that she didn't know where anything was.

"I . . . um . . . have a soufflé in the microwave." She cleared her throat, wishing her voice didn't sound so squeaky.

"I hear they fall if they're not tended to correctly."

His breath was tantalizing her, touching her neck and making it very difficult for her to swallow. And she had to swallow. The dryness in her throat was unbearable. "Yes, they do," she agreed.

"Everything around you requires your care and feeding, doesn't it?" he asked, his eyes still holding her where she was. He was making her think of delicious things just by sitting there and looking at her.

"Yes, it does."

"Do you like having things dependent on you?"

"I don't think the soufflé minds very much."

She knew they weren't really talking about anything as inconsequential as a soufflé. They were talking about him. In his own strange way, he was opening up to her. He was giving her a coded message about himself. A message she had already begun to suspect. He wanted to keep control over everything that he was relinquishing into her hands. Didn't he know that was impossible? She'd never be able to get anything done, and he might as well not have her around if that were the case. And suddenly C.J. wanted to be around, even though she knew she couldn't allow what had just happened to happen again. It was an aberration, a weak moment brought on by the hour, the situation and her swaying sofa.

She rose on shaky legs. "The soufflé can hardly be expected to get out of the oven itself."

"No, I guess not," he said, watching her walk into the kitchen. The woman was far too well built for her own good. For his own good.

He didn't know what had come over him just then. He had tried to pull back at the last moment and hadn't been able to. There was something about her that drew him to her. Drew him to her, yet warned him to be cautious of her at the same time. He couldn't shake free of the way he felt about women. All women. Could she see how he felt? Would she use his vulnerability against him?

He should just fire her; then he wouldn't have anything to worry about.

No, he didn't want to fire her. He needed her, damn it. This whole matter was getting too complex for him to deal with right now. And he was tired. Very, very tired.

"Mind if I stretch out for a minute?" he asked, leaning back against the dark, fuzzy, swaying sofa.

"No," C.J. called out from the kitchen. "Make yourself at home. Although I have no doubt you will whether I tell you to or not," she said with a grin, echoing his words to her the first time she had walked into his house.

"How do you feel about spinach soufflé?" she asked, taking two potholders from their hooks on the wall. She opened the oven. The soufflé was perfect, high in the middle and sloping down slightly on either side.

"Never had any feelings about it one way or another," he answered, his voice a low mutter.

"You will after you try a piece. I make a mean soufflé."

"Go after everything with a vengeance, don't you?"

His voice sounded muffled, and she wondered if he was being sarcastic. "Just my nature," she answered lightly. "My brothers were all very strong willed, and I wasn't all that much bigger than they were, even when they were young. It took a lot of force to get them to do the things they were supposed to do." She smiled fondly as she set the soufflé in the center of the small kitchen table. "By now, they're all taller than I am and—"

She stopped. It was very quiet. Too quiet. "Travis?"

There was no answer. Quietly she walked over to the sofa.

"Son of a gun," she muttered to herself, a soft smile playing on her lips. He had fallen asleep.

"What a headline for a magazine this would make," she said under her breath as she went to fetch an extra blanket from her bedroom. She draped the blanket around him slowly, careful not to wake him. "*Hot star falls asleep on personal manager's water sofa*. Doesn't sound as innocent as it is, does it?" she asked the sleeping face.

She sat down on the edge of the sofa for a moment. Even though she tried to do it gently, the sofa swayed. Travis murmured something unintelligible in his sleep and continued dozing. C.J. curbed the urge to brush the hair off his face.

"What's your story, McQuade?" she wondered out loud. "Why is control so important to you? And why should letting me do a few simple things for you get you so uptight?"

There was nothing but the sound of his even breathing to answer her. C.J. rose and went to eat her soufflé.

She finished dinner and put away the dishes, and Travis went on sleeping. She walked back into the living room and stood looking down at him for a long moment.

"Well, I guess you're here for the night, huh?" She thought of waking him, then decided against it. "Clementine Jean Parker with the country's newest heartthrob sleeping in her apartment. Who'd have thunk it?" She laughed softly to herself as she looked down at his face. The dim light lovingly caressed his features, and she longed to do the same. But she didn't.

Relaxed, his face looked younger, carefree. He probably looked, she surmised, the way he had when his agent had discovered him in an ad.

"So what am I going to do with you?" she murmured softly to herself. "How am I going to do my work if you're constantly fighting me? And what made you come back after I quit?"

On the surface the answer was simple enough. He obviously needed her. She knew it. He knew it. But maybe, she thought, the rub lay in the knowing.

Maybe he was a fiercely independent man who couldn't bear to have people handle things for him. "You're in the wrong business, then, McQuade," she whispered to him.

He stirred faintly, and she smiled despite herself, running her fingers absently over her lips. It wasn't going to happen again, she told herself. But that didn't mean she couldn't linger over the memory. He was every woman's dream done up in a bow.

"Every woman's but mine," she said aloud, as if to convince herself. "Good night, cowboy. Pleasant dreams."

With that, C.J. turned off the lights and went to bed.

Six

_____

Travis spent a restless night.

He dreamed that he was on a pirate ship, caught in a rough, merciless sea. As he wandered about the deck, he saw that the ship had no crew. Slowly, however, the crew began to materialize. Women. Everywhere he looked there were women who turned and smiled at him as he passed, women who watched him with hungry eyes. As he walked, he was aware that each woman left her post and began to follow him. Soon there was a legion of women, all smiling, all hungry, all trailing him.

He was terrified.

He picked up speed. They matched it, pursuing him relentlessly, until he fell down a ladder into the interior of the ship. He tried to hide, but they found him each time. He went deeper and deeper into the belly of the ship, until he was finally cornered. There was nowhere to turn, nowhere to run.

And still they came. Except that they were no longer beautiful women. He was horrified. Right before his eyes, a metamorphosis began taking place. Slowly the women were being transformed into black widow spiders, spinning webs to trap him, ready to devour him, for he was their mate and he had to die.

He yelled as he struggled to keep them from touching him.

C.J. bolted upright. What was that? Travis! She had left him asleep on her sofa. What in heaven's name could have made him yell that way?

She dashed out of her room, still half-asleep herself. He was sitting up, breathing heavily, his eyes closed. C.J. took hold of his arms to steady him.

His face was soaked with perspiration.

"Are you all right?" she asked.

He opened his eyes, drawing a long breath to steady himself, then nodded, a bit embarrassed. C.J. released her grip and sat down uncertainly on the edge of the sofa.

"Just a dream." He tried to dismiss it with a wave of his hand, but the shaken expression on his face told C.J. otherwise.

She gave him a sympathetic look. "Sounded more like a nightmare."

"It was," he admitted without elaborating. He didn't want to discuss it. It exposed his inner feelings and made him feel very vulnerable. "I must have fallen asleep." The words were sheepish.

She took her cue and let the matter drop. "Sure looked that way," she quipped.

He looked at her for the first time since he had bolted up from his nightmare, ready to apologize for falling asleep on her sofa, but the words were never formed.

C.J. suddenly realized that she hadn't put on her robe when she'd dashed out of her room. All she was wearing was a sky-blue teddy. Sky blue, like his eyes. Except that his eyes weren't sky blue right now. They were the color of opaque smoke, skimming over her, touching her softly, as if he had never seen her before.

"I...um..." C.J. Parker, glib talker, got no farther. She was mesmerized by the look in his eyes and by the feelings that were spreading within her.

A moment before he had dreamed of being devoured by his female fans. There was no other explanation for his dream. Women were going to make him their latest victim, another mindless hunk who fell by the wayside. And now here he sat, still shaken, suddenly attracted to a women who had, however unintentionally, made his existence miserable for the past two weeks.

Get up and get the man coffee, she commanded herself. Do something!

She couldn't move. All she could do was sit, trembling slightly, on the edge of the sofa. Just the sway of the water, she insisted to herself. But she wasn't sure.

Something else was swaying, swaying from within, vibrating with a need that stunned her.

God help me, I want him.

The thought shocked her. What was the matter with her? She tried to rationalize her feelings. It must be the situation, the hour, the outfit, maybe even the new benjamina. No, she forced herself to admit, it was the man.

Framed in the dawn light that was seeping into the room was a breathtakingly handsome man. There was a very obvious reason Travis McQuade had become the crown prince of hearts. It had been a long time between such genuinely sexy leading men.

It was a sensuality, a sexual quality, that was honest, unpretentious, instinctive. It was evident in everything he did, without any conscious effort on his part.

She watched as he reached out for her. She shouldn't let this happen again, yet she knew she couldn't pull away if her very life depended on it. Slowly, his eyes never leaving her face, he slid one strap off her shoulder. She was infinitely aware of its descent, her eyes held fast by the look on his face. It was hypnotic, but if she were put to the test and asked to describe it, she couldn't. It just *spoke* to her, called to something inside of her. Something that she couldn't quite give a name to.

The second strap slipped down her arm, and with it went the bodice of the teddy, until the whisper soft material floated down to the hardened peaks of her breasts, hanging there tremblingly.

Get up! Move! she screamed silently, but she stayed. Waiting. Anticipating. Fearing.

His long, delicate fingers buried themselves in her hair, then gently pulled her toward him. C.J.'s lips parted.

When his lips touched her it was with incredible gentleness, despite the charged tension that filled the air. She wasn't even sure that he *was* kissing her, his touch was so soft.

And yet she had never been more sure of anything in her life. She could feel herself responding to him. She felt as if a volcano had erupted within her body. C.J. couldn't keep her hands at her sides. She curled them around his arms, assuring herself that this was real, that he was real. Hard muscles met her touch. Muscles that were rigid, as if to belie the gentleness of the kiss that met her lips.

The kiss deepened, his lips brushing against hers with a building intensity, until suddenly she was totally swept away by her own desire.

Travis, too, was in the grip of something uncontrollable. A moment earlier he would have sworn an oath that women were at the root of all his trouble, and that C.J. herself was merely a necessary evil in his life. And now...now he felt consumed with a hunger so intense that he couldn't begin to comprehend it. He couldn't remember ever feeling quite like this before. He had never wanted a woman so much. He knew by the way her body bent toward him that he could take her, take her here and now, on this incredibly ridiculous swaying sofa. Take the woman he resented, though he brought trees to her instead of letting her go.

It was a riddle far more complex than his dream had been.

C.J. felt the pressure of his mouth lessen, his hands loosen from behind her head. Something had made him stop. Something had brought back his good sense just as she had abandoned hers.

She felt grateful and pained at the same time.

She fought hard to regulate her breathing. Quick, she ordered herself. Say something before he realizes that you were ready to give him much more than your salary allows for. "I...hope...you're not parked—" better, her breathing was much better "—in a tow away zone."

He looked at her, relieved that she was so quick. He forced himself not to look at anything but her face. She didn't look quite the same as she had a moment ago. Her lips were still imprinted with his, a rosy hue smudging the perfect lines of her mouth. And there was a bright flush in her face and a shimmer in her eyes.

"The doorman parked it for me."

She rose on incredibly unsteady legs, surprised, in a way, that she could stand at all. Her knees felt numb. "If it was Jake, he probably took it home with him, to fantasize over."

"It wasn't Jake." Travis swung his legs off the sofa, running his hand ruefully through his hair.

"No, of course not." Was that her voice? It sounded so nervous. "It was late, wasn't it? Jake gets off at—"

"Look, Clem," he began, raising his eyes, giving her a soul melting look, "I'm sorry—"

No, don't apologize, she pleaded silently. Not for what just happened. Don't spoil it. It won't ever, ever happen again, I promise. Just don't spoil it. "Nothing to apologize for. You're not the first man to fall asleep in a strange place because he was tired. Put some coffee on, will you, while I get dressed." She eased out of the room gracefully.

He almost stopped her as she began to leave, almost gave in to the gut-wrenching feeling that leaped up at the sight of her moving away so sensuously. He knew she wasn't doing it on purpose. There didn't appear to be a deceitful bone in her body. She had looked too stunned when he had kissed her, too stunned when he had stopped. There were a host of things she was, but a calculating female like the ones he was used to was not one of them. She probably had no idea just how desirable she was, or how close she had come to being made love to.

He crossed to her kitchen and tried not to think of the fact that she was shedding the silken, flimsy material just a few feet away from him. "Clem, where's the—"

"In the pantry, next to the cereal. You know, that funny stuff you won't eat."

He smiled. One jump ahead of him, as usual. He had been right to come over last night. She hadn't deserved that outburst yesterday afternoon. If only she weren't so—so damn perfect. He'd have to learn to control his temper, or whatever it was that made him act the way he did around her.

She came out ten minutes later, looking as if nothing had happened between them other than the exchange of a ficus and an unplanned nap on her sofa. She smelled of soap and freshness. It made him ache.

"Any chance of my grabbing a quick shower?" A cold one, he added silently.

C.J. glanced at her watch. "Every chance in the world," she told him. "We've got plenty of time—and I just put out fresh towels," she added with a broad smile.

He went to wash up, leaving C.J. to try to sort out her thoughts. She gave up before he closed the bathroom door. There was no sorting this out. They already had a business relationship, tumultuous though it was. There was no room, no need, for any new developments. He'd had a nightmare and sought momentary comfort in her arms. Whatever he had dreamed, it had frightened him. Children cried when they had bad dreams. Sometimes adults turned the bedroom lights on to ward off their nervous feelings. He had kissed her. There was nothing more to it than that.

Oh, but there was. There was.

C.J. began moving briskly around the kitchen, getting breakfast ready, as if to deny the little voice within her.

He was grateful to her, he thought later that day, for acting as if nothing had happened. He had been wrong about her. She wasn't insensitive. Just, he thought wryly, incredibly bossy. That nothing could change. But, then, maybe she was like that because of the type of work she did. He didn't know what personal managers were supposed to be like. He'd have to be more tolerant.

That was easier said than done.

The director was reshooting a minor scene, and Travis had retreated to his trailer, tired. He walked in just as C.J. was hanging up the phone. She saw him come in and bit her lip.

Something was up, he thought. She always bit her lip just before telling him something, usually something he found himself not liking. He forgot about his determination to be tolerant.

"Curt's secretary called a little while ago."

He was surprised. His publicist hadn't used a go-between since Travis's star had risen so quickly. The man always called himself. "What did she want?"

"Curt's in the hospital."

"The hospital?" he echoed. "What—"

"Nothing serious," C.J. said, lowering her eyes and doodling on the pad in front of her. "Appendicitis," she explained. "I already sent him flowers from you."

"Thanks." That wasn't all, he thought. "Anything else?" he probed.

"Yes."

He knew it. "What?"

C.J. hesitated. She would never have hesitated with anyone else she worked with, but she knew that every step she took seemed to bother Travis, and she had just stepped into a mine field. Seeing to his publicity wasn't exactly in her realm.

"I was just on the phone with Alex Bellamy."

"His office?" he asked, confused.

"No, him."

How had she managed that? Alex Bellamy was the host of the most popular late night show in the country. While others had come and gone, their places taken by late night movies, Alex had tenaciously remained the crown prince of insomniacs for nearly twenty years. Rather than become slack or stale, his appeal seemed to grow with the years, as did his loyal fans.

"Curt's secretary gave me his private number. Bellamy called Curt about you, but Curt was already in the hospital."

"Go on."

His tone, she thought, was rather tight, as if he were waiting for something. A bomb to be dropped. He expected her to say something that he wouldn't like, didn't he? she guessed. Damn him, anyway. Any normal person would do handsprings over what she was going to tell him.

"He wants to interview you," she said in a rush. "I set it up."

"You did?" His expression was growing darker by the second.

"Yes."

"Without asking me?"

"You were in the middle of a shoot," she pointed out, exasperated. "Alex Bellamy isn't the kind of man you put on hold and do well with afterward. And I don't think the director would have been overly pleased if I'd run out in the middle of his taping, waving my hand like some idiotic schoolgirl."

She was right, of course, and he was being unreasonable again. But that didn't change the way he felt. He had to have a say in matters that concerned him. He couldn't just allow himself to be swept along like a mindless puppet. Puppets were discarded when they were no longer amusing.

"Damn it, Clem, you could have found a way."

"I left my carrier pigeons in my other purse, and I'm not much on charades."

"Okay, okay, you made your point," he muttered, trying to suppress his anger. Why did she *always* have to be right? "But I don't know how I'm going to get the time to—"

"It's all arranged."

"Naturally." The word dripped with sarcasm. She had found a way when he couldn't see one. Travis sat down and laced his fingers together behind his head. "All right, tell me."

"He's bringing a crew here during your lunch hour."

"Alex Bellamy?"

"Yes, unless I was talking to a damned good impressionist."

It was tantamount to someone telling Noah that God was dropping in for tea to talk about the measurements of the ark. It seemed impossible. He could remember watching Bellamy's show when he had taken a job as a night watchman at the warehouse. His feet hurting, his career up against an endless succession of doors that wouldn't open, Travis had sat and watched Bellamy's show night after night, promising himself that someday he would be up on that dais, sitting next to that trim, witty man and talking to the world.

And now it was happening. It was incredible. It had been almost three years since his star had shot up into the heavens, and he still wasn't used to it.

"And just how did you manage to get him to come here?" he wanted to know.

"It wasn't hard," she told him with no sign of false modesty. C.J., he had learned, was nothing if not straightforward. It was one of her better qualities, one of the ones he could cope with. "He's a big fan of yours."

"Alex Bellamy?"

"Alex Bellamy. In case you haven't noticed, the man is pushing fifty, isn't as fit as he used to be, and probably loves to live vicariously through Paris's adventures. He's got money, but he doesn't have your—" she stumbled for a moment, only because she herself had almost fallen victim to them this morning "—attributes, shall we say? I told him about your shooting problem and suggested that if there was any way possible, perhaps he could tape your segment here."

"He doesn't run taped interviews."

C.J. shrugged, getting up. "Have it your way. I guess his crew *won't* be arriving next Tuesday at noon, and he *won't* be here to talk to you." She eyed him, waiting for his response.

"Clem—"

She held up her hand. "No need to thank me," she said cheerfully, cutting him off before he could say anything to the contrary. "Just doing my job. See you later."

"Where are you going?" he asked suspiciously.

"It's lunchtime."

"And you're going to eat lunch?"

"I was planning to, yes."

"Just lunch?"

Her eyes narrowed playfully. "Why? Was there something else you wanted me to devour?"

No, he thought. You can devour anything you want, just as long as it isn't me. "Have a good lunch," he muttered.

"I intend to. And oh, yes, you're welcome," she quipped as she closed the door behind her.

How did you say thank you to someone who invaded your life? he wondered. Made it better, but invaded nonetheless? A benevolent dictator was still a dictator. A kindly jailer still a jailer. And C.J.... C.J. was a living, breathing example of capability and competence—and the most exciting, intriguing, attractive women he'd ever met.

The phone rang, and he was tempted to ignore it. Probably the Pope calling C.J. to tell her that Travis could have a private audience as long as she arranged it, he thought sarcastically.

Three rings later he picked up the receiver. "Yes?" he barked.

"Caught you at a bad time?"

It was Peter. Travis took a deep breath, then let it out slowly. "No, just things getting a little hectic, that's all."

"Oh?" Peter sounded disappointed. "I called to see how things were going. Isn't C.J. helping alleviate any of that?"

"Oh, yeah, yeah." What she wasn't alleviating were his feelings of resentment—and plain old-fashioned lust. "She's just a wiz."

Peter caught his tone immediately. "Travis, what's wrong?"

"Nothing's wrong," he snapped, then immediately felt sorry. "Pete?"

"Yes?"

"Is she on something?"

"On something?" Peter repeated, puzzled. "What do you mean?"

"You know, does she take anything?"

"Not that I know of. Why?"

"No reason," Travis answered. "It's just that she never seems to slow down."

"Oh, that," Peter laughed. "That's part of C.J.'s charm."

"I think you're stretching the word."

"Give her time, Travis. She'll get to you," Peter promised before he hung up.

Travis stared at the silent receiver before he hung it up. "That's just the trouble," he said softly to no one in particular. "I think she already has."

Seven

A week passed. They both made an effort to be more in tune with each other. The one thing they seemed to be mutually, if mutely, in agreement on was how to treat the incident in her living room. Neither mentioned it. Both pretended it hadn't happened. And both were plagued by thoughts about it at unguarded moments.

But the unguarded moments were few and far between. The series' hectic pace blotted out almost everything.

"Your life certainly is one great big whirlwind, isn't it?" C.J. muttered, easing her neck against the headrest in his sports car. It was going on ten o'clock at night. The crew had been working doggedly all week in an effort to wrap up the week's taping in five days for once, instead of six. They had reached their goal half an hour ago.

Lights from passing cars occasionally lit the interior of the Ferrari. She glanced out, absently watching the flow of traffic. Everyone seemed to be in such a hurry. She saw a bright yellow Buick whizz by, its occupants apparently cruising the streets looking for Friday night amusement.

All C.J. wanted to do was get into a hot bath and then crawl into bed. One look at Travis's face told her that he had the same thing in mind. She smiled to herself. The town's most popular hunk, and all he yearned for was a quiet evening at home. He had a lot of likable qualities, she thought. If only he weren't so pigheaded at times.

"Hmm?" He suddenly realized she had said something that required an answer. He hadn't really been paying attention.

Actually, neither had she. It was just something she had said in passing. "Skip it. It wasn't important." She continued to stare out the window.

The song on the radio ended and a commercial came on, advertising the opening of a new movie the following week.

Travis was tired, but not too tired to realize that C.J. had straightened up in her seat. She made him think of a dozing fox that had just smelled quail. Now what? he wondered.

"Sounds like a good movie," she said as the strains of another song began to surround them.

"It is." He remembered how much he had wanted the leading role, but Berenstein had told him he would be committing professional suicide to take on the role of the psychopathic killer.

He felt her staring at him. "Tom Convy's a lucky son of a gun to have landed it," he added vaguely.

"It wasn't all luck, I'm sure," she said.

"No," he agreed, feeling as if she were hunting for something. "Talent was there, too."

"I wasn't thinking about talent."

Dared he ask? "What *were* you thinking about?"

She turned in her seat. "Push, drive, things like that."

"Clem," he began wearily, sensing vaguely what was coming next. Lately he'd found himself more and more in tune with the way her mind worked. The possibilities were frightening. "You can push all you want in this town, but the doors have to be swinging in the right direction."

"So change the hinges."

"What?" He pushed his hair back from his forehead. "Look, maybe it's the hour, but you're making less sense than usual."

"Tell me something honestly." She was getting excited, and she knew that the tempo of her speech increased in direct proportion to her excitement. She also knew that Travis had difficulty absorbing her words when she went into high gear. With an effort she switched from forty-five to thirty-three and a third RPM.

He eyed her warily. "What?"

"Do you want to risk becoming last year's hunk?" She knew she was on dangerous ground, but she also knew that, despite everything else, she was involved with this man, on whatever level she chose to admit it. She didn't want to see him wasting his life. "*Paris Cassidy* could last another season. Maybe five. Then what?"

"And then we'll see what happens," he said evenly. He was aware of the fact that he was arguing against his own beliefs. What purpose would it serve to let her know he had been badgering Berenstein about the very same thing? That was a private matter, one not up for discussion. And besides, right now all he wanted was peace and quiet.

C.J. didn't feel sleepy anymore. "What will happen is that you'll become another Grant Goodale. Oh, maybe not as paunchy—" her eyes slid over his taut physique, which even beneath clothes and at the end of a hard day, was still magnificent "—or a dried out drunk, but what will there be for you? Third-rate roles in low-budget pictures? Horror movies?"

"Clem!" He raised his voice.

"What?"

"Can it."

She crossed her arms in front of her. "You can stop me from talking."

"How? How?"

She ignored his sarcasm. "But you can't stop it from happening unless you *do* something."

"Tomorrow, right after I get up, I'll send in my application to the Royal Shakespeare Company."

"Sarcasm isn't going to get you anywhere."

They stopped at a red light. "No," he said, looking at her, "but adhesive tape might. Applied right here." He ran his finger along the outline of her lips.

He had merely meant to stop the flow of words from continuing. Instead, touching her served to table the budding argument in another fashion. He hadn't come close to touching her since that morning after his nightmare. Now this slight physical contact vividly brought back everything he had been trying unsuccessfully to bury.

"I'll put adhesive tape on my shopping list," she said quietly.

"You do that," he said softly. A horn blared behind them.

"You're holding up traffic," she pointed out. "You'd better get going."

"There you go, giving orders again." But he was smiling as he said it.

"Facts," she said, her voice low and teasing. "Just stating facts."

They rode in silence for a few minutes, something tangible hanging in the air between them, something neither wanted to deal with just yet.

A romantic song punctuated the silence. Travis switched the dial. The country and western station he chose had a singer bemoaning the state of almost lovers, almost friends. This time C.J. changed the station. Rock music hit the air like cold water, relieving them both.

"It's not like I'm inundated with good parts, Clem," he finally said.

His voice was tired, and she got the feeling that there was more bothering him than just an overloaded work schedule.

"Producers like sticking with a sure thing."

"So they won't let you do *Macbeth*," she surmised dryly.

He grinned. Even highlighted in the glare from passing cars, it was a beautiful smile. "Not a chance."

"There are other parts with depth," she said philosophically.

"And they go to other actors."

"Fight for them," she told him.

"They're gone before I even get word they're around. Besides, that's Berenstein's territory."

"Well, he's been leaving it uncultivated."

"Clem, I'm having a hard enough time coping with what you're doing now. Don't go overboard." Stop overwhelming me, he continued silently. Stop being Superwoman. Just be what you are—a beautiful, desirable woman.

She smiled, trying to sound flippant. "Not to worry. I promise to behave." Somehow he needed to be pushed in the right direction. It's not your area, C.J. Let it go, she warned herself.

The silhouette of his house loomed before them. She hadn't realized they had traveled so far. "Well, here we are, the old homestead. I'll just get my notebook and be out of your hair." She got out quickly, trying to camouflage her thoughts. Sitting so close to him had made her want to touch him. Touch him and *be* touched by him.

"If only I could believe that."

C.J. stopped walking up the driveway and turned around. "Do you mean that?" she asked seriously.

He dug into his pocket for a key, pretending to be occupied by the act. "No," he admitted quietly. "I don't."

She had practiced sorcery on him. As much as he still wanted to be his own man, to handle his own life, he was beginning to feel he couldn't function quite right without her, even after such a short period of time. It wasn't so much a case of what she did for him as it was the fact that she gave him something to look forward to. Their daily verbal sparring kept him on his toes, made him feel alive and vibrant. She was like a megashot of B12. He wondered how she'd react to being likened to an injection.

And like an injection, he went on thinking, flipping on lights as he walked into the house, there were still plenty of times when she was a pain in the place where doctors most liked to give injections.

"I'll just be a minute," she promised. She glanced around and saw her notebook on his coffee table. She was getting sloppy, she admonished herself. "If I don't throw some cold water on my face, I'm going to fall asleep at the wheel while I'm driving home."

He hesitated. "Do you want to spend the night?"

"Definitely not," she said too quickly, then hunted for words to smooth over the moment. "I don't sleep well in strange beds."

"I can sleep anywhere," he told her as she walked to the bathroom.

She thought of the endearing way he had looked on her sofa. A warm feeling spread through her. "Yes, I know."

Wash your face and get out of here before you give in to yourself, she warned herself silently.

C.J. marched into the first bathroom on the right and dropped her things on the black onyx counter. She turned on the antique brass faucet full blast. She cupped her hands, catching the cold water, then dashing it into her face.

There, that felt better. As she reached for the hand towel hanging on the side of the sink a movement behind her caught her eye. She could have sworn the black-and-gold shower curtain had moved.

You're just tired, she insisted. Your eyes are playing tricks on you.

But she saw it again, despite her attempt to reassure herself. The curtain was definitely moving.

A burglar?

No, that was ridiculous. Burglars didn't hide in showers. They dashed out of the nearest exit and ran with whatever they had stolen. There was nothing to steal in the bathroom—unless you were hunting for souvenirs.

That was it!

C.J. walked up to the shower, steeled herself and swept back the curtain. A wide-eyed girl of no more than sixteen gave her a weak smile. C.J. dropped the curtain and walked out.

She found Travis in the kitchen, making a chicken salad sandwich. The skeletal remains of a chicken, an open jar of mayonnaise and scattered leaves of lettuce were everywhere. The man was a mess. He looked up when she walked in.

"Did you leave a girl in your shower?" she asked wryly.

"Was she dressed?"

"Yes."

"Then I didn't." He plopped a thick piece of white bread on top of a mound of chicken salad and lettuce. "You're serious, aren't you?" he said in sudden realization.

"Yes."

"How, why—"

"The how is that you have no security system. The why is, of course, you." She walked back to the bathroom, Travis hot on her heels. "You can come out now," she called, holding the door open.

The girl looked both frightened and overwhelmed at the same time. She stared at Travis as if he had just crossed the ocean without the aid of a boat. "It's really you," she squealed.

"Yes, it's really him," C.J. said, taking the starstruck girl's arm and leading her back to the living room.

The girl twisted her head, unable to take her eyes off Travis. "In the flesh." The girl sounded as if she were gasping for air. Travis smiled at her. It only made things worse.

"Takes it wherever he goes," C.J. told her, picking up the phone.

When the girl realized what C.J. was doing, she came out of her trance. "Oh, please don't call the police." She clutched at C.J.'s arm, horror-stricken. Another thought came to her, one that was apparently even worse. "Or my parents!"

C.J. finished pressing the buttons and looked at the thunderstruck girl. "Any objections to the cab company?"

The girl blinked, looking from Travis to C.J. in confusion. "What?"

"I'm calling you a cab."

"I'll pay for it," Travis told her.

"Anything you say," the girl gushed.

C.J. had the good grace to keep from laughing out loud.

The cab arrived within ten minutes, and C.J. sent the girl off clutching an autographed picture of Travis in her damp hands.

"And don't try that again," she called after the departing cab. The girl was hanging out the open window, determined to look at Travis until the last possible moment. "He's getting a new security system put in. Wolves! Trained to kill!"

"Colorful, aren't you?" Travis asked as they walked back inside. He closed the door behind her.

"I try," she said. "But you *are* getting a security system put in."

"I am, huh?" At this hour he was too tired to argue.

"Yes, you are. That girl's mouth will be working all night. By morning you'll be inundated. There will be nubile young things scattered for as far as the eye can see, scaling walls and hiding in your shower." She glanced at him. "Scaling you."

"Would that bother you?" He had no idea what had made him ask.

"Depends," she answered noncommittally.

"On what?"

"On whether they got to you before you wrote out my weekly paycheck."

He brought his chicken salad sandwich over to the living room and put the plate down next to her forgotten notebook. "You're a strange creature, Clem."

"'C.J.,'" she repeated patiently. "I'd really appreciate you calling me 'C.J.'"

"Life doesn't always give you what you want, Clem," he said lightly.

She laughed. What was the use? He did it just to get her. "I'm beginning to see that. Well, I'd better be—"

"Share a sandwich with me?" he interrupted. For some reason he didn't want her to go. "I make a mean chicken salad sandwich." A leaf of lettuce fell out of the proffered delicacy.

C.J. picked it up from the coffee table. "I can see that. I thought you were dead tired."

"Finding a strange girl in my shower always perks me up." He sat down, patting the seat next to him.

C.J. complied, taking the half a sandwich he offered. What would a few more minutes hurt?

"How do you suppose she got in?" he asked. "I didn't see any broken windows."

"Never underestimate the power of a palpitating heart, McQuade. She probably came down the chimney in hopes of filling your stocking, or whatever else was available."

"Like my shower."

"Like your shower. Hmm, this is good." She took another bite, finishing off the piece he had given her.

"How long do you suppose she was there?"

"Who knows? Maybe since morning."

"That long," he marveled, his mind barely on the conversation. "That seems ridiculous."

"You underestimate yourself. From what I read in your fan mail, women would gladly stand in the broiling desert sun for a week, wrapped in cellophane, just for the chance to see you smile."

He brushed away a crumb that was clinging to her mouth. "And how long would you be willing to wait?"

His face was so close that thinking was becoming difficult. "I never gave it any thought."

"Think." The word swept across her lips, along with his breath.

"Oh, maybe fifteen seconds."

"I didn't think you'd even wait that long," he told her just before he kissed her.

This time the kiss was not a study in gentleness. Not that it was rough, just intense. She could detect a definite need there, which excited her beyond reason.

He put his hands around her waist and drew her to her feet as he stood, still kissing her. His hands slipped down to her hips, molding her to him just as his lips molded themselves to hers.

C.J. felt helpless. She knew she should put a stop to this. It was ridiculous to let it happen again. And yet she couldn't stop it. She didn't want to. She let herself be swept away by the force of his kiss.

A moan of pleasure—or was it pleading?—escaped her as she felt his hands move upward to the sides of her breasts. The ache and need she felt sprang up simultaneously.

Touch me, she pleaded silently as his hands slowly moved, until they slipped between her breasts and touched her nipples, which had tightened into hard buds beneath her light silk blouse.

C.J.'s breath became audible, and her pulse hammered like thunder in her ears as she pressed closer. He had power over her, she realized in a daze. Power like no other man ever had. With just a look, a touch, the barest of kisses, he could make her hunger like a starving creature unfed for an eternity.

She felt the outline of his tongue as it lightly glossed over her lips, parting them and taking the succor that she offered so generously.

She wanted to touch him, to make him hers, to make him feel the same way he made her feel.

No, damn it, no, her saner side insisted. This isn't a competition. Get away now. You're his manager, not his mistress.

The word *mistress* was far more enticing, far more inviting.

Just as she felt herself reaching a point of no return, he drew back slightly.

He looked as confused as she felt, but she took advantage of the moment to call a halt. "You were right," she said, swallowing hard in an effort to alleviate her breathlessness.

"About what?"

"You do make a mean chicken salad sandwich." Slowly, discreetly, she took one more deep breath. "Well, it's late. I'd better go home." Before I do something stupid, like throw myself into your arms again. "I'll see about getting that security system installed tomorrow."

"Tomorrow's Saturday," he reminded her as they walked to the door.

"Yes, I know. And all the high school girls are home." Trying to remain detached and friendly, she tapped his cheek lightly. "Think about it."

"I am," he said softly as he closed the door behind her. "I am."

He stood leaning against the door, staring off into space long after she had left. He wondered what she thought of him, calling an abrupt halt like that to what had been building between them. His behavior had probably confirmed her belief that he was difficult and crazy. But he had never felt passion take possession of him the way it had with her tonight. Except, perhaps, that morning in her living room. Each time he kissed her, he felt an overwhelming need to have her, to make her part of him. To make him feel whole.

He couldn't accept it, just as he couldn't accept his need to keep her in his life.

But it was there all the same.

Refusing to think about it, he went off to bed.

Eight

C.J. considered getting a key to his house one of the major triumphs of her career to date. Getting a key had always been standard operating procedure with her other clients, but her dealings with Travis never followed the normal route. He had balked at the idea originally, but he'd felt, right after he had rehired her, that a show of good faith was necessary. So he had gotten her one. Or, more accurately, he had allowed her to have one made.

She used it for the first time the day after they discovered the girl in his shower.

It was a Saturday, and Saturdays off were rare for Travis. He wasn't lazy by nature, but this Saturday he had promised himself that he would stay in bed until noon. Maybe longer. He had earned a long rest.

It was a promise made without taking C.J. into account.

It wasn't any particular noise that woke him. It was more of a general feeling that he wasn't alone. He woke with a start, then lay there, listening for something to confirm his suspicions. The girl in his shower had made him paranoid, he told himself, glancing at the clock.

Nine o'clock. He hadn't stayed in bed until nine since . . . well, since he couldn't remember when. He stretched his long, powerful body, feeling ridiculously happy for no apparent reason.

He stopped in midstretch. There it was again. Voices. He was sure of it. Damn if C.J. hadn't been right. That girl they had found last night must have told her friends. They had returned en masse.

He bounded out of bed, ready to put a stop to this newest invasion. Then he looked down, suddenly remembering what he was wearing. Or wasn't wearing. He grabbed his robe from the foot of the bed, recalling the look in C.J.'s eyes when she had first seen him in his cutoffs.

The thought of C.J. made him smile unconsciously. She was the greatest enigma he had ever stumbled across. He felt hopelessly attracted to her, yet resolved to stand his ground and resist her on all levels. Having C.J. around was definitely not dull. What it was was damned exhausting, he thought, tying the sash of his robe firmly around his middle.

With that he marched out, prepared to evict any and all invaders. C.J. was right. He did need a security system. C.J. was *always* right. C.J. was—

C.J. was there.

His mouth opened in surprise, but no words formed as he looked at the people in his living room. C.J. was standing in the middle of the room with two men, pointing animatedly as she spoke. The shorter of the two men was writing every word down. It probably pleased her to no end, Travis thought, having someone listen that intently. He cleared his throat loudly.

C.J. whirled around, startled. "Oh, I'm sorry. Did we wake you?"

"No, I always try to get up early when there's a convention being held in my living room," he replied curtly. "Clem, what the hell's going on?" He walked into the room. "Who are these people?"

"Travis," C.J. began patiently.

There was that tone again, he thought, the one she used when it sounded as if she were speaking to a child who required infinite patience. It threatened to make him lose his.

"I'd like you to meet the Johnston brothers. Tom—" she nodded at the shorter of the two "—and Frank." The man with the beard extended his hand toward Travis.

"Watch your show all the time," Frank told him.

"Don't own a TV," the other said rather proudly.

"Good for you," Travis said to Tom tersely. "Clem—" he put his arm rather roughly around C.J.'s shoulders "—can I see you for a minute?" With that he pulled her over to the side.

"I can walk under my own power, McQuade," C.J. said, shrugging off his rough hold.

"You seem to be able to do a lot of things under your own power. Who *are* these people?" He glanced over his shoulder. Tom and Frank were busy conferring, Tom taking notes on the large yellow pad he held.

"They're going to install your new security system," she answered.

"*What* security system?"

"The one we decided you needed after Miss Hollywood High invaded your inner sanctum last night," she answered breezily.

There was no point in arguing that he didn't need one. He did, and he relinquished the round to her. But did it have to be today?

"Couldn't you have held off the Invasion of Normandy until Monday?"

"I could have, but I'm not too sure you could. If I've learned anything at all about you in these past turbulent weeks, it's that you value your privacy."

That sure hasn't stopped you, he thought.

"As I explained last night, I'm sure that by now Barbie has told Ken, Midge and a whole crowd of people how she got to see Travis McQuade in person. I don't think we should wait with this." She gestured toward the two men and what they represented. "Do you?"

He sighed. "Would it matter if I did?"

"Well-ll—"

He didn't wait for her to say anything further. He waved a surrendering hand in the men's direction. "They're here. You might as well get on with it."

"Knew you'd see it my way," C.J. said cheerfully, turning toward the men.

"Clem, with you there *is* no other way." A sigh of resignation escaped his lips. He nodded toward the men. "Are they good?"

"I wouldn't get you anything but the best," she told him.

He said something unintelligible as he walked into the kitchen, and C.J. thought it best to let it pass, whatever it was.

The installation turned out to be an all-day job. Travis didn't exactly know what he'd planned to do with his hard-earned day of freedom, but hanging around while a security system was being installed in his six-bedroom house was not it.

He worked on his lines until noon, then called a friend and arranged to play doubles at the man's estate.

"How long are they going to be here?" he asked C.J., stopping in the den on his way out.

She glanced up from the schedule on the desk in front of her. Her answer lingered for a moment on her lips as she looked at him. His dark tan was striking against his crisp white shorts and pullover shirt. The sleeves of the shirt were taut against his biceps. It was the kind of sight that fans bought binoculars for and waited all day to glimpse. She was careful not to let her admiration show.

"As long as it takes," she answered, trying to sound casual.

"That's what I like about you, C.J., you're always so definite."

"Don't worry," she assured him, "I'll stay here until they're through. You going out like that?" Her eyes swept over him slowly.

He was aware of the way she was looking at him. "Yes, why?"

"I thought you didn't like getting mobbed."

He smiled. "I'm playing at a friend's private court."

"What other way is there?" she mused, looking back at the schedule she was planning.

He should be going, he told himself. Instead he perched on the edge of the desk, twirling his tennis racket between his fingertips, an amused expression on his face. He caught her meaning. He had certainly moved up in the world. "In a way, all this is pretty fantastic," he agreed with her.

There was a tanned, muscular thigh right next to her hand, and C.J. had to control an urge to run her hand along it, to run her hand along all of him. He did things to her, broke her concentration, made her want things she had absolutely no business wanting. She had been around movie stars for the past five years, but he was the first one who had practiced his magic around her without meaning to, and she had been caught up in it. All the others had tried to impress her with their importance and failed to evoke anything but vague loyalty from her. He, with all his stubbornness, *with his gentleness,* had captured her heart almost immediately.

"Five years ago I was a hungry cowhand from Montana. Now I'm playing tennis on private estates and having a security system installed in order to keep lovestruck fans out." He shook his head, as if dazed by it all. "Doesn't seem real."

"Reality is what you make it," she answered, wishing he'd get up, wishing he'd take his thigh away before she allowed herself to do something horribly out of character and totally stupid.

Ever since he had kissed her last night she'd been experiencing the most overwhelming desires. She had come within a hairsbreadth of staying last night, and the urge, even in the light of day—or because of it— was still there. Nothing, she realized, was going to dampen it, but her own self-control was going to have to help her keep it under wraps.

"You're sitting on next week's schedule," she told him, tugging at the piece of paper under his thigh. She was careful to keep her fingertips from touching him.

He hopped off her desk, oblivious to her inner turmoil. A turmoil he had caused. "Oh, make a note on that. I want time to do an appearance on a telethon."

"When?"

"Next Saturday night."

She jotted down a note. "I wasn't aware that there was a telethon being held then."

"What? Something slipped by you?"

For once his sarcasm was welcomed. It took the edge off her desire, at least a little bit. "Apparently," she answered dryly. "Which one?"

"Leukemia Society. At 7:00 P.M."

"I'll clear time with the director and get you off the set by five," she promised.

"That's what you're good at."

Finally! He'd given her credit for something, however left-handed the compliment. "So long as you know," she murmured, turning back to her work.

"See you."

And he was gone.

It was a long time before the Johnstons were gone. It took a long time to install the security system properly. There was no rushing good work. She was the first to acknowledge that. Her own work for the day had long since been finished. She had planned his week, as well as her own. Hers went on for pages. She'd made a note to get all the questions that Alex Bellamy might ask Travis ahead of time. She didn't want Travis to risk being embarrassed, although she was sure that at this point in his career he could sit on the show reciting nursery rhymes and it wouldn't matter. Not to his female fans or the daydreams and fantasies they had about him.

She wandered over to his video room. C.J. felt a headache beginning over the bridge of her nose. She had been concentrating too hard. She was restless, she decided; she needed some diversion. A light and entertaining movie would fit the bill.

She glanced through the tapes he had. They were scattered around the room, some piled on the table, a few on the sofa, two on the video recorder. There was a perfectly good cassette cabinet going begging in the corner, with only two tapes to fill its numerous slots.

C.J. began gathering the tapes together, alphabetizing them as she went.

She discovered that he had videotapes of the two movies he had made, *Soldier Stands Alone* and *Here Comes Culhane*. She held the two tapes, one in each hand, deciding. You couldn't get much lighter entertainment than this, she thought, putting *Soldier* down and inserting *Culhane* into the VCR. She closed the shutters and turned the machine on. Sinking down on the nine-foot sofa in front of the large screen, she let her mind drift as she began to watch.

Here Comes Culhane was a typical detective story. Unlike *Paris Cassidy*, it was set in the twenties, complete with speakeasies, bathtub gin and flappers.

And Travis.

He towered head and shoulders above the others, in stature, in looks and in performance, she thought. The others appeared to be just walking through their parts. Travis's character was so stirring in his intensity, so lovable in his foibles, that she found herself *really* watching, *really* enjoying what she saw. She had never bothered to see the movie when it was playing in the theaters a year ago, and now she actually regretted it.

The female lead was terrible, C.J. thought critically. Even *she* could have done a more creditable job.

C.J. leaned back against the sofa. Her muscles ached. She was tired. You're trying to do too much again, she admonished herself. She had gotten up early to drive over to the Johnstons' private residence to talk the men into coming out and working on a Saturday. She was acquainted with them because of work they had done for two of her previous clients.

She'd been aware of their reputation, and knew that their fee matched their expertise. But Travis set high store by his privacy; she knew he wouldn't mind paying to keep it. And the sooner she got the job done, the better.

But now she was tired, terribly tired. She leaned back on the deep sofa and pulled her legs under her, relaxing. The heroine had just been rescued by Culhane, and now, as soft, romantic music wafted through the air, he was making love to her....

He was making love to *her*. C.J. stood holding her breath, waiting for it to finally happen. Slowly Travis was kissing her as her clothing dropped away, piece by piece, burned away by the fire in his eyes. He wanted her. She felt the pressure of his hard body against hers, demanding, urgent.

"I've wanted you from the first moment I saw you." The dialogue from the film filtered into her dream as she slept. "There's no point in torturing ourselves any longer by denying what we feel."

Oh, God, yes, yes. Love me.

And then his mouth was on hers, hot, wanting, drawing out her very soul.

C.J. moaned.

"Ms. Parker? Ms. Parker, are you okay?"

"Travis?" she murmured.

"No, it's Tom."

C.J.'s eyes flew open and she flushed, embarrassed. "I...dozed off for a minute."

"Well," Frank said, with a pleased smile, "now you can do that without fear of being bothered by any undesirables."

"Oh, I don't sleep here. That is…" She realized that both men were looking at her, trying to hide knowing looks. And why should they think any different? She had fallen asleep, and when they had wakened her, the first thing out of her mouth had been Travis's name. She decided that it was fruitless to deny anything. "Thank you so much for coming out," she said, rising. "Now if you'll just give me a basic rundown on how everything works…"

That was embarrassing, she thought after the men had explained everything to her and left. Returning to the video room, she flounced back down on the sofa and turned the tape back on.

Travis and the heroine were still enmeshed in their love scene. C.J. felt her cheeks growing hot as she watched. She wasn't sure if it was because she was having a vicarious experience, or because she felt— what? Jealousy? Why should she be jealous? She and Travis had a strictly professional relationship—with a couple of lapses in between. But that didn't mean anything.

Face it, she told herself. You want it to mean something.

Well, whether she did or not was beside the point. She couldn't allow herself to indulge any of her desires. Any of…

Her mind began to drift again as she put herself into the heroine's place. She was so engrossed that she didn't hear him come up behind her, had no knowledge of him until he put his hand on her shoulder. And then she screamed and jumped.

"Hey, it's only me," Travis said laughing. And then he became serious. "I didn't mean to scare you."

"Sorry." She was embarrassed at her own skittishness. "It's just that I thought I was all alone."

"Houdini brothers gone?" he asked, sitting down next to her.

"They're gone." She hadn't activated the alarm system, since Travis wouldn't have been prepared for it and would have set it off when he returned. "Let me show you how the system works and then I'll be on my way." She began to stand.

He caught her wrist. "No hurry. Why don't you finish watching the movie? As a matter of fact, mind if I join you?" He sat down just as he glanced at the screen. He hadn't realized what she had been watching, and now he winced.

"Not if you can stand it," she said, commenting on his involuntary reaction, not the movie.

"What made you pick this?" he asked, waving at the screen. "I've got a lot of other tapes."

"I know. I put them all in order."

"Always tying up loose ends," he observed, but for once there was no sarcasm in his voice.

"I try."

"Sometimes," he said, turning toward her, "you try a little too hard."

"Guilty," she admitted.

He was looking at her closely. She hadn't been out of his mind all day. He had called it an evening early, leaving the impromptu party and hoping that she would still be there when he returned home.

Was it all there in his face? he wondered. All there for her to see? "It's pretty bad, isn't it?" he said, looking back at the screen.

"The story is, but you're not."

"Loyalty," he quipped.

"Truth," she corrected.

He turned back to look at her. The light from the screen turned her hair almost platinum, tempting him to touch it. "Do you always tell the truth?"

"Always."

"What would you do if I kissed you again?" he asked softly.

She felt her pulses go haywire. Say something flippant, her mind insisted, but she couldn't. "I'd kiss you back."

"I see," he said quietly, his fingers slipping under her hair. "Let's put that theory to the test."

The kiss drugged her, seeping into her like sparkling wine, drenching her nervous system. It masked her doubts, shrinking them until they faded away. All that was important at this moment was Travis, the thrill of his touch, the warm promise of his body. Gentle fingers caressed her curves, igniting depth charges at every point. Her breathing grew shallow, her desire fathomless.

"I'm glad you stayed," he murmured along the curve of her throat.

"I had to," she said, trying very hard to sit still. Her mind was reeling drunkenly. "I couldn't leave while they were still here. And then I had to wait to explain the system to you." Well, explain it already and go, she ordered herself, but she wasn't listening. She stayed where she was.

She felt his fingers gliding down the front of her blouse. He played with the top button for a moment, then opened it. Then he opened the next one. And the next, until the blouse hung open. "Maybe I'm lucky you're so conscientious." His mouth just barely touched the planes of her breasts as it passed.

"I keep trying to tell you that." The words were uttered breathlessly as C.J. felt all the air leaving her lungs. She struggled to regain it. He was draining her, making her mindless.

With a light touch that belonged to an artist, he ran the back of his hand softly over the upper swell of her breasts. Every part of her ached for more.

One hand stroked her back, gentling her as if she were a nervous filly. She could feel her limbs grow heavy as excitement built within her. She sensed his fingers gliding slowly along the back of her bra. He was searching for the clasp. She felt herself smiling against his mouth.

"It's in the front, isn't it?"

C.J. nodded.

"Always trying to be difficult, aren't you?" he teased.

This time she shook her head. Never had she wanted to be more cooperative.

As he coaxed her lips open with tiny, sensuous kisses, C.J. could feel that he had run into further problems with her bra. She was tempted to take it off herself and be done with it, but his hand felt so wonderful brushing against her as he tried to release the clasp. Finally he used both hands.

"This could give a man a complex," he told her, his voice low and brimming with barely checked emotion.

She was about to answer, but her words were stolen away, pushed aside by exquisite sensations. His mouth moved to her neck, causing magnificent things to happen inside her as he slowly kissed her. The two halves of her bra had been released. She felt them being eased away, succumbing to the rhythmic motion of his hands, which were massaging her gently, driving her crazy.

As the material parted farther and farther on either side, Travis lowered his head and began to cover the exposed area with a shower of kisses. With each kiss the cups retreated a little more, until finally the bra slipped, useless, away from her breasts.

She buried her fingers in his mass of wayward hair and pressed his head down slightly, urging him on. C.J. moaned as his tongue gently touched one nipple and then the other, making them hard, making them ache for the fullness of his mouth.

When he raised his head again to look at her, she felt a shiver of disappointment go through her. Don't stop now, she begged silently. Please.

"We're reaching the point of no return," he told her softly, giving her a last chance to call a halt if she wanted to.

Her eyes drifted to his mouth, then back to his hypnotic eyes. Behind them, on the screen, triumphant music swelled as Culhane bested six or seven opponents. "What makes you think I want to turn back?" Her voice was husky with desire and wanting.

There was nothing more to be said. He took her into his arms, holding her close, feeling her heart hammer within her breast as he kissed her inviting mouth.

This was crazy, and he knew it. He was giving in to the power he felt she had over him. But he couldn't rid his mind of her. He had played the hardest game of tennis in his life, as if to blot out the demons that haunted him, as if to blot out the face that haunted him. And he had been powerless to do so, just as now he was powerless to deny the hold she had on him.

He motioned her back for a moment, stripping his shirt off and tossing it aside in one fluid movement. "I want to feel you against me." His voice was low, caressing her just as surely as his hands had done. He lifted her blouse, letting it drift down her arms before he tugged it away. And then he guided the straps of her bra from her shoulders. It, too, dropped to the floor.

He held her against him, his lightly haired chest faintly tickling her breasts as he swayed, his passion mounting. C.J. curled her fingers on his shoulders, digging in. He was raising her passion to an explosive level.

Letting his hands drop to her buttocks, he massaged her slowly, raising the hem of her skirt by inches until it was nearly at her waist. A moist, hot throbbing began between her thighs.

"Travis."

She whispered his name, her voice low and filled with desire. It was the first time she had spoken his name with such emotion, and it drove him over the brink. There *was* no turning back anymore, no denying the intense desire he felt. He was trapped, trapped by his own needs, trapped by her. He hated it, yet he gave in to it, because he wanted her, needed her, just as he needed to breathe in order to live. She was a basic need in his life.

The skirt dropped to the floor, joining her other things.

"Come sit on my lap," he urged softly. His will was hers.

He pressed his head against her aching breasts, caressing them with his hands and his tongue. C.J. squirmed, desire beating a surging, molten path through her entire being. His eternally questing hand skimmed lightly along her spine as he kissed her, sending sparks shooting through her. He found the perimeter of her panties, playing with the elastic for a moment, sliding his finger back and forth before finally slipping it beneath the band and lightly touching her.

C.J. drew her breath in sharply, then let it out in a soft, surrendering sigh.

"Lift just a little."

She heard the words in a hot, melting haze.

She must have done as he asked, because the next thing she was aware of were her panties sliding along her skin. And then his hands, his wonderful hands, kneading her, touching her, leaving her moist and wanting, needing him.

He pressed her back into the sofa. Somehow he had shed the rest of his clothes. His hot, searing flesh pressed against her as his glorious, warm mouth explored, teased, tantalized and drove her mad. It seemed to C.J., as she gave herself up to the swirling passion that Travis created within her, that every time he touched her, he made her want him that much more. Want? No, it was a craving, an obsession beyond belief.

She made love to the man who had brought her a tree, to the man who had awoken, shaken and pale, on her sofa, to the man whose liquid blue eyes she had gotten lost in. The man whose face was etched with passion. It was as if a rainbow were spreading out within her, a rainbow whose slivers of light burst into glaring rockets as Travis's hands caressed her body, making love to her.

When he entered her, it was with an unbelievable gentleness, as if he were afraid to hurt her, afraid to shatter the moment. But then, once they were joined, their passion built into a frantic melody. They clutched, held and moved with a wildness that startled them both, breaking barriers they had never even admitted existed.

Nine

Oh, C.J., what did you do?

C.J. slowly rose on her elbow. There, next to her, the sheet wrapped around his waist, was Travis, sound asleep. They were in his bed. It was the middle of the night, or perhaps closer to morning; she wasn't sure. The room was dark except for a light sprinkling of moonlight filtering through the curtains.

The euphoric haze that had enveloped her last night was gone, replaced by the cold grip of reality.

What had she allowed to happen? This wasn't like her, to give in to her desires, to let her feelings get in the way of her job. How was she going to work with him now? It would have been different if they'd had an easy relationship to start with, if things had gone smoothly between them. But given the constant power struggle they seemed to engage in every time she opened her mouth, this was going to make things impossible.

Impossible. That was the word for him, all right.

She looked down at his face and felt her desire stirring all over again. Last night came back to her in flaming highlights. He had made love to her on the huge sofa in his video room, then gently carried her to his bed, where they'd made love again. And again. There had been no sign of the brooding, impossible man she had grown to know. There had been only a gentle, thoughtful lover who brought her to heights she had never experienced, stirred her emotions to depths she had never felt.

If she hadn't known better, she would have said she was in love with him, she mused as she studied him and tried to absorb everything about him.

She did know better. She knew the truth. She *was* in love with him. And oh, what a mess that was going to make of her life. She sensed that he had some sort of a love-hate relationship with his female fans, and for some reason the way he felt spilled over into their working relationship. She was very aware of the hostility he seemed to bear toward her at times, and she had wanted that out of the way before anything happened between then. She realized then that she had always felt that something *would* happen between them, despite their clashing personalities. Or maybe because of them.

Well, it was too late to wish things had happened differently. She was just going to have to wait and see how they developed.

"I'm the best thing that's ever happened to you, and you don't even know it," she said softly.

He stirred a little, as if he were putting up an argument, even in his sleep.

He would, she thought fondly.

She would have liked to remain where she was, slipping back into the warm cocoon she had occupied just a short while ago. But she was afraid that once he woke up a different light might be in his eyes from the one that had been there last night. The light of embarrassment, perhaps. Last night might have been an aberration, brought on by who knew what. When he looked at her, she wanted to see an echo of the emotions she felt, not embarrassment, not unspoken apologies, and not, heaven help her, hostility.

It would be best if she left now. When she saw him on Monday, after he had had time to deal with what had transpired between them, there would be time enough to face him.

Maybe she needed a little time to herself, as well, to think things through.

Quietly she slipped from his bed and ventured back into the video room. She turned on a small side lamp, then looked over her shoulder to see how far the light reached into the hallway. She didn't want to wake him.

Nothing stirred. Good.

Quickly she collected her clothes and began getting dressed. She threw her blouse on first, stuffing her bra into her purse, then reached for her underwear.

"Going somewhere?"

C.J. whirled. Travis was leaning against the doorway, looking a little bemused, his arms crossed over his naked chest. The cutoffs that he had hurriedly donned on his way out of his room hung rakishly low and unzipped on his hips. The sight made her stomach quiver.

"I thought it would be best if I went home."

For a moment he said nothing as he uncrossed his arms and came toward her. He took the underwear she was holding out of her hands. "Sometimes," he said, letting the panties drop from his fingers onto the sofa, "you don't know best." He bent his head, kissing the slope of her neck. "Come back to bed," he murmured against her skin.

She felt herself melting against him, grateful for the fact that he was holding her. She wasn't all that sure at the moment if her legs could support her.

"Are you sure?" she asked. A lot went unspoken in her question.

Unspoken, but not unfelt. Rather than continue the discussion, Travis picked her up in his arms again. "Clem, why must everything between us turn into a debate?" he asked, carrying her back into his room.

C.J. put her arms around his neck, snuggling closer. "I was on the debating team in college," she told him, picking up the subject playfully. She felt gloriously happy. "My team always won."

"I never doubted it for a moment." He put her down on the bed and covered her body with his own, lacing her fingers with his over her head.

"McQuade?"

"Hmm?"

"Get rid of your shorts."

She felt his grin forming against her lips.

"Y'know, Clem, some of your suggestions aren't half bad."

She hadn't been sure exactly what to expect on the proverbial morning after. But she was glad as she sat opposite him in the kitchen, wearing one of his sweat shirts and eating the French toast she had prepared, that he wasn't sporting a look of regret. It was more like a look of confusion, she decided, as if he couldn't quite find a place in his life for what had happened last night and this morning.

No matter. She could wait, she thought happily, swishing her last piece of bread around in the sea of syrup on her plate. What would be would be, she told herself. With maybe a little help from her on the side.

"What are you smiling about?" he asked, breaking into her thoughts.

"Just that I love—French toast," she ended impishly, popping the last piece into her mouth. Travis leaned over and licked the drop of syrup that clung to her lips. It was all the excuse that was necessary.

She had never made love on a kitchen floor before.

C.J. couldn't remember when she had hated a Monday morning more. Monday brought with it the routine pattern that their lives had fallen into. It was as if the weekend had been locked away, a fairy tale that had happened and was now over. A brief, wondrous respite from their daily lives. They were back in their respective corners, she with her efficiency, he with his wariness. Nothing had really been resolved. The only thing that had changed was that they had openly admitted the intense attraction they felt for each other.

C.J. promised herself that resolutions were going to be in the offing. Soon.

Monday morning, after several phone calls, C.J. managed to get hold of the questions that Alex Bellamy planned to ask Travis when he came to do the taping on Tuesday. After waiting for an appropriate break in the hectic shooting schedule, C.J. presented Travis with the two-page list.

A makeup man stood hovering over him, trying to repair any damage that the fight scene Travis had just shot had done. Travis waved him back for a moment, quickly scanning the two sheets C.J. had given him.

"Where did you get these?" he wanted to know. Bellamy liked to spring surprise questions on his guests. That was what made his interviews so intriguing. They weren't the routine "how's-your-life, tell-us-about-your-latest-picture" fare.

C.J. grinned, proud of herself. "I called in a few favors," she told him. "I know a lot of people in this town."

And how many knew her? he wondered. Knew her the way he had come to know her this weekend? Had she had many lovers? Did what had happened between them mean as much to her as it did to him? Ever since they had made love, he had found his obsession for her growing, and with it, a nagging resentment at the additional shackles that this new need added to the chain that bound him to her. Women had dictated that his career stay where it was until they grew tired of him. And now a woman was taking over the helm of his life, making appointments for him, telling him what to do and when to do it. Putting words into his mouth. And making him want her as he had never wanted anyone else.

He tried to shake the dark mood that was coming over him.

"Thanks," he muttered, knowing he shouldn't act this way, but unable to help himself.

She hadn't exactly expected him to do handstands. But she hadn't expected him to sound so removed, either. Why was he acting this way?

"Travis, we're ready," the director called out.

"Be there in a minute. Here—" he stuffed the list back into her hands "—hold this for me."

"Sure." She wished she could get inside his head and find out what was going on in there. One minute he was the sweetest man in the world, incredibly tender, making her love him so much that it hurt. The next minute he looked at her as if she were the enemy, making her doubt her own perceptions. She couldn't figure him out.

The interview took place in Travis's trailer the following afternoon, during a break in shooting. C.J. saw to it that everything went smoothly. She swept the Minicam operator and Alex Bellamy, with his personal entourage, into Travis's trailer with an incredible amount of ease. After it was over she took the Bellamy people out to lunch, saying that it was on Travis. They ate at one of the most exclusive restaurants in the area, and she could see that even Bellamy was impressed by Travis's thoughtfulness.

She explained to Bellamy that although Travis would have loved to accompany them, he had to beg off because he had four more pages to shoot that day. There was no way he could get any more time off, having already promised the director his firstborn in order to tape the interview.

Bellamy laughed, to her relief, and insisted that C.J. sit next to him during the entire meal. It was clear to his entourage that he had taken a liking to the snappy, bright-eyed blond.

That afternoon roses were delivered to Travis's trailer. He saw the delivery boy go by and absently wondered why his fans were sending him flowers now. But why not? They sent him everything from home-made cookies to knitted sweaters to X-rated home videos of themselves.

A few minutes later the director turned his attention to a minor scene. Travis took the opportunity to go back to his trailer. C.J. was there, arranging the flowers in a vase she had purloined from the prop department.

He read the card: "Thanks for an amusing lunch." He looked at her, confused. The card was addressed to C.J. The flowers were from Bellamy.

"How did you amuse him?" he asked, feeling a strange sensation in the pit of his stomach. Jealousy?

"I was my usual charming self," she answered lightly, closing the box and tossing it into the trash. "Some people seem to like that."

The look in her eyes challenged him to say something.

He glanced down at the card on the table. "Yes, I can understand that. Are you going to see him?"

"Sure."

"Oh."

She couldn't resist teasing him. "I wouldn't miss watching your broadcast for anything. Don't forget, while it was being taped, I was busy juggling yes-men and trying to find places for everyone to sit." She shook her head, hands on hips. "That man has more people following him around..."

Travis took her hands from her hips and replaced them with his own as he fit her against him. Bellamy hadn't gotten to first base with her. He felt a sense of relief surging through him. "God, there's only one way to stop you from talking, isn't there?"

C.J. grinned as she looked at his lips. "Best way I know of," she answered, just before he kissed her.

They had to watch the interview on the television set he kept in his trailer. Filming that day had taken an exceptionally long time. The director, in a fury of creative ire, had ordered three new pages written. A whole scene had to be reshot to accommodate the new pages, and everyone was exhausted by the time the day was over. They had worked well past ten.

"I might as well live in this trailer," Travis complained. "We have to be back in less than eight hours."

She wasn't fooled for a moment. He loved to work. But even workaholics got tired sometimes. "You need to relax," she told him as she walked over to the phone.

He watched as she picked up the receiver. Who was she calling at this time of night? "What are you doing?"

"Sending out for some dinner. Chinese."

She had hit on his favorite again, he thought. She always seemed to know exactly what to do to make him feel better. He supposed he *was* a little crazy to resent having someone around who sensed his every need. Just because there was an army of women out there who thought of him as a commodity, a thing, an object to lavish their affections on until the next bright new face came along, didn't mean that C.J. was like that.

If only he could get rid of this feeling of being cornered. He had gotten this far in his career through no particular doing of his own. It was his looks that had carried him. It was his looks that women reacted to. And now another woman was reacting to him, another woman was doing her best to ensure the future for him that she thought best. And he was letting it happen.

What was wrong with him? Was it that he was afraid he wasn't good enough to do anything else, to trust his own instincts? What had happened to the man he used to be?

Sometimes he felt as if he had lost the thread of his own personality, yet she always seemed to know exactly what she was about.

What *was* C.J. like? he wondered. He didn't know very much about her, except what little she had told him that first day and the bits and pieces she'd let drop since. She was probably a sorceress in disguise. She had certainly turned his life upside down.

And straightened it out in the process. Don't forget that, the fair side of his mind reminded him.

How could he? That was part of his problem.

He sank down on the sofa, exhausted more from his mental gymnastics than the day's work.

C.J. hung up the phone. "Turn around," she ordered, walking over to him.

"What?"

"I said turn around."

"Why?"

"My God, you are the most difficult man to deal with." Forcibly she turned him so that his back was to her. She got on the sofa behind him, balancing on her knees. "I just want to rub your shoulders, that's all. You make it sound as if I'm going to mug you."

"With you I never know what to expect." Her hands felt wonderful as they kneaded away the tension. He angled himself closer.

"Just service, McQuade. Good, efficient service."

"Was that what the weekend was about?" he asked quietly. "Service?" The thought had been nagging at him. He had been around so many opportunists. He had to know that she was different, had to hear it from her lips.

He felt her hands drop from his shoulders. When he turned to look at her, the expression he saw was one of pure fury. Her eyes smoldered as she tried to find the right words. "Now you listen to me, Travis McQuade. I don't care what your title is—"

"What?"

She sprang from the sofa, pushing her hair away from her face. "—whether you're the 'crown prince of hearts,' as the magazines say, or what you might be able to get from all those women the studio keeps turning away at the gates every day. This weekend was *not* business as usual. I *don't* go to bed with my clients."

He'd had to hear it from her, had to hear that things were different between them from the way they'd been with other people she'd worked with. He'd had to know that she hadn't done it merely for the thrill of going to bed with "this year's hunk." "You did with me."

"Is that what you think?" she cried. "That I went to bed with you because—because—oh, damn!" She hit him, a fly swinging at a prize fighter. "You make me so mad. I wish I were a man."

Her eyes told him all he needed to know. It *had* been different between them. Now that she'd said it, he was relieved. He could let his feelings go. "It wouldn't have been half as much fun if you were."

For a moment C.J. just stared at him, stunned by his swing in mood. He was going to drive her crazy. Well, not tonight.

C.J. grabbed her purse and flew to the door. Or tried to. But he caught her wrist before she could reach for the doorknob. He had to forcibly turn her around to face him. She was feistier than he had thought. Also stronger.

"Let go of me, *Paris Cassidy*, or you won't be able to finish taping the last show of the season standing up straight,'' she threatened, her voice near the breaking point.

How could he? How *could* he think that what happened between them was something that had sprung out of some sort of insane job definition? Or worse, that she was some mindless little thrillseeker who'd merely wanted to go to bed with the man millions of women dreamed about? She *cared* for him. Couldn't he see that? Was he so blinded by mindless adulation that he couldn't see the difference between wistful fans and a woman who was in love with him? *Him*, not a screen image!

''If I let go of you, you'll leave.''

''Damn right I will.''

He pressed her against the wall, leaning in closer. ''And then I won't be able to kiss you.''

She wanted to retort with a cryptic comment, wanted to hurt him as much as he had just hurt her. But all she could say, with his mouth so close to hers, was, ''Would that matter to you?''

''Yes. Very, very much.''

Her arms went around his neck without her even knowing it. She rose on her toes to press her lips against his more fully. His hands slipped around her waist, pulling her into him, imprinting her with the fierce wanting that had sprung up in his body.

''I'm sorry,'' he whispered. ''But I had to know.''

She saw the look in his eyes. Beyond the desire she saw a troubled man, a man who had been swept into the vortex of such adulation that he had trouble sorting out what was real from what was illusion. She understood, and she nodded as she let her fingers toy with the buttons of his shirt.

"Now you know," she said quietly. She leaned her cheek against his chest. "Now you know."

The knock on the door broke into the peaceful, pregnant silence. "Dinner," C.J. guessed, turning to open the door.

A tired-looking delivery boy shuffled in, carrying two huge paper bags. C.J. took them from him, holding them against her. She stifled a yelp. The food was still piping hot.

Travis paid the boy, then turned around as C.J. began taking out container after container. "We're going to eat all this?"

"Got to keep your strength up," she said cheerfully, digging through the bag for the plastic forks that were buried on the bottom.

He took the forks out of her hands and pulled her close to him, then kissed her quickly. "I see your point."

C.J. laughed. "Not now. The show's going to be on in fifteen minutes."

"That doesn't give us much time, does it?" he asked, his hands moving sensuously along her waist.

C.J. popped an egg roll into his mouth. "No, so start eating."

He let go of her waist and devoured the egg roll. "I'd rather do something else."

"You start that," she said with a wink, "and you're sure to miss the show."

"Always giving orders, aren't you?" he asked playfully, nuzzling her neck.

She laughed. "You smell of egg roll," she said. "And as for giving orders, that's what you pay me for, to look out for you."

"Don't look out too hard," he said, sitting down. "I can take care of myself."

The tone was playful, but she caught the message.

"Travis, there was never any doubt in my mind that you could. All I want to do is help." The serious look left her face. "Now eat your *moo goo gai pan*."

"Yes, ma'am."

"Better," C.J. announced playfully, approving of his display of mock obedience. "Much better."

He wondered just how she meant that.

Ten

Ten minutes before the program began, there was a knock on the door.

"Are you expecting anyone?" C.J. asked. She moved aside two cartons and set down her container of sweet-and-sour pork.

"Not at this hour."

"Maybe it's one of your zealous fans," C.J. cracked, opening the door.

Grant Goodale, still wearing the scruffy outfit he'd had on during the day's taping, stood in the doorway. "Hi, mind if I watch with you?" he asked, nodding toward the TV. "I'll never get home in time to catch it."

Travis waved the burly man over to the sofa. "You've seen the worst side of me on the set. I guess I can stand to have you watch this."

"If I don't watch," Grant said as C.J. switched on the set, "I'll probably be the only person in the country who misses this."

"Pull up a container," C.J. urged, pushing several opened white cartons toward Grant.

"I think you're exaggerating," Travis said, mumbling into his *moo goo gai pan*.

"Can you believe it?" Grant asked C.J. as she joined them on the sofa, perching on the arm next to Travis. "The guy's modest. Thousands of women willing to kill for his nail clippings, and he doesn't let it get to him." A reminiscent smile slipped across the intentionally grizzled face. "Hell, when I was in his shoes I couldn't get enough of the good life." He picked up a carton and stirred the contents absently. "No eating out of little boxes for me. I lived high." He laughed to himself. "I found it a high place to fall from, too." There was no self-pity in the remark. There would have been once, but Grant had learned to appreciate what he had now instead of living in the past. He attributed that to Travis.

The introductory music to *The Alex Bellamy Show* had faded, and the suave, elegantly groomed man walked out from behind the curtains.

"Shh," C.J. said to Grant. "I want to hear this."

"She wants to gloat," Travis explained to Grant.

"Gloat?"

"She's the one who got me the questions ahead of time."

Grant laughed heartily, his stomach shaking. "You've got an angel in your pocket, Travis."

"Only problem is, she keeps trying to crawl out," Travis commented.

"Will you two be quiet?" C.J. implored.

"A grumpy angel," Grant amended.

Bellamy's opening monologue was over. The audience had been receptive, and he looked quite content with himself. "And tonight," he said, "We have a little treat for you ladies. Travis McQuade—"

A roar went up from the studio audience.

"My God, get the whips out, men," he said with a laugh, pretending to talk to someone offstage. "Sorry, ladies, before you leap out of your seats, he's not here in the flesh."

A moan greeted his words.

"No, the man works so hard he could only phone in his interview. Actually, we have more than his voice," he went on with the elfin smile that had become his trademark. "We have him on tape, grilling him, if you will, so that you ladies can see the man behind the image."

"He sounds like one of those cheap tabloids," Travis commented, nibbling on a chicken wing.

"He sounds like he could give your career a push in the right direction," C.J. pointed out.

"She's the one who's always pushing, you notice that?" Travis asked Grant. He forced a smile, trying to make up for the slight edge in his voice.

"Listen, if I had someone like her in my corner, maybe I wouldn't have gone to seed the way I did. Everybody I ever met always wanted a piece of the action. They never wanted to add to the ante." Grant smiled, reaching across Travis and his chicken wing to give C.J.'s knee a squeeze. "Don't you let him out of your sight, C.J. The big idiot needs you."

"He needs some quiet," Travis said, calling for a halt in the discussion.

C.J. winked at Grant and put her finger to her lips. "Shh, the boss has spoken."

Travis tossed the chicken wing into an empty carton on the table and pulled her down on his lap. "And don't you forget it."

The tone was teasing, but there was no mistaking the underlying seriousness of his words.

"You're not my boss, McQuade," she said, her voice low, but firm. "You're my client."

He played with a strand of her hair, sifting it through his fingers. "Same thing."

"No, there's a difference."

"You two gonna talk through this whole thing?" Grant asked. "The cat's stopped dancing for his supper." He jerked a thumb at the screen. "Bellamy's introducing you."

They fell into silence. For the next fifteen minutes, the television provided the only sound in the large room.

After it was over Grant pushed his food aside, stood and stretched. "Well, I've gotta be going. Thanks for letting me watch with you." Travis was still sitting, although C.J. had gotten up. Grant put his large hand on Travis's shoulder. "Great interview." He nodded at the set. "You got a great future, kid. Don't mess it up." He glanced at C.J. "Any of it. Good night, all."

"You don't seem very excited," C.J. commented after Grant left. "You want me to shut this off?" She placed her finger over the On-Off switch.

Travis nodded. He was obviously deep in thought. "It did go rather well, didn't it?"

"Rather well? It was terrific!" C.J. smiled as she sat back down next to him. "You held your own very nicely, despite the deep, probing questions."

"That's only because you—"

"No," she said firmly, putting her finger on his mouth to silence him. "It's not only because I got you the questions. I got you an edge, but the answers were yours, not mine. You were the one scoring points up there, not me. I think you earned his respect—and quite possibly let people see the more serious side to Bounty Studio's 'Hunk of the Year.'"

He winced at the nickname that had been given to him in a recent movie magazine story. Idly he leafed through the script that was lying on the table next to the Chinese food. He wasn't really looking at the pages. He *had* looked good up there tonight, he thought. He hadn't come across like the empty-headed pretty boy so many people thought he was. He had sounded intelligent, in control. The thought brought a slight smile to his lips.

"You really don't look as excited as you should be," she repeated.

He stopped thumbing through the script. She had done this for him. She had helped, no matter how much she denied it. "Maybe that's because I save my excitement for a certain blond-haired lady who makes my blood rush even though she insists on arguing about everything.''

"I don't insist on arguing. You—"

"See? You're doing it again." He grinned, knowing he had won his point. Then the look in his eyes softened. "Let's celebrate," he proposed. His voice lowered. "Stay with me tonight."

"Here?"

"Here, in my car, in the middle of Hollywood and Vine. I don't care, as long as you're with me." He felt an overwhelming passion seize him, just as it had the first time. And the second time. And the third.

"Don't you want to go home?" she asked.

"Suddenly I can't wait." He cupped her face with his hands, kissing her eyes closed. He could feel her body turning to liquid against him. Liquid gold, he thought, his kisses deepening as his hands slowly massaged her back, her hips, her breasts. Impatience clawed at him.

He raised the hem of her sweater, gradually working it up past her waist, tantalizing her with it, trying to hold back the flood of desire that was consuming him.

C.J. raised her hands over her head, letting him pull the sweater free. His eyes met hers. "Do you always react this way when you've had a successful interview?" she asked, her voice a whisper. His hand was on her stomach, making it quiver in response to his gentle touch. As the zipper of her slacks slid down, C.J. could feel herself melting. Touch me. Touch me all over. I belong to you. The words rang so loudly in her mind that she was amazed he couldn't hear them.

He pulled her against him. "This is the way I seem to act with you," he said, pressing his mouth against hers.

Not always, Travis, she thought regretfully. Not always.

She couldn't think any longer. He was laying waste to her mind as his hands stroked her, rendering her helpless. Her body slipped into a flaming haze fashioned by his ardent kisses.

"McQuade, I think we—"

"Shh. Just once," he said, putting his finger to her lips, "stop thinking, stop talking. Just feel."

There was no need to tell her that. She *was* feeling, feeling a wide spectrum of wonderful sensations and longings as his hands slid along her hips, pushing aside her slacks. He assaulted the corners of her mouth with tiny, tempting kisses that exploded inside her.

She tilted her head back, thriving on the feel of his lips on the delicate expanse of her throat. Sensuously erotic feelings tantalized her as his mouth moved on, kissing the rosy peaks of her breasts that rose to meet him.

Where had her bra gone? Where had the room gone? Nothing remained except for him. His clothes had somehow melted away, and his body, firm and hard, pressed her down into the sofa.

Everywhere he touched her turned into an erotic zone. Each time he made love to her, C.J. thought, a force even greater than before seized her. If her passion grew any stronger she felt sure she would burn out totally. They would find her, an exhausted shell of her former self, dying in his arms.

There were worse ways to die.

But she wasn't about to die alone. With a spark of mischief still alive, C.J. turned the tables on him. Pushing Travis back, she laced her fingers through his, keeping his hands above his head as she kissed him slowly, sensuously. Loosening her fingers, she forged a trail of kisses along his chest. Her path led her steadily downward.

She lingered for a moment around the few dark silky hairs that led to his navel. She flicked her tongue along his abdomen, feeling his smooth skin tremble just the tiniest bit. His newly freed hands caressed her shoulders, his rhythm duplicating the rhythm of her stroking tongue. As her movements brought her lower, C.J. heard his sharp intake of breath and then felt the gentle pressure of his hands as they raked through her hair. A flood of electric heat soared through her as she continued raining kisses on him, doing things she had never even fantasized about. Being with Travis demolished all the barriers she had ever set for herself. Everything seemed pure and natural when she was with him.

She was driving him into a frenzy of desire. "C'mere, you," he ordered hoarsely, taking her by the shoulders and raising her back up to him. The passion with which his mouth seized hers was equalled only by the force with which his body merged with hers. C.J. cried aloud, but the cry transferred itself into his mouth. As she clung desperately to him, a veritable light show went off in her head as she rode with Travis to journey's end.

The lights began to fade, but C.J. had no energy to even open her eyes. She wished there was a way to hold on to the exquisite sensations that his lovemaking created. She wished that there was a way to hold on to *him*. But she knew it would be like trying to hold a sliver of mercury. It was impossible. There was something holding them apart. Something inside him. Until he bared his soul to her, until he told her what it was that stood silently between them, it would always be like this. She would always have a piece of him, but not the whole.

C.J. strove hard to keep her sadness at bay, but she barely had enough energy.

Travis, on the other hand, seemed to have lots of energy. He was stirring next to her, pulling on his clothes. She pried open her eyes and stared at him accusingly. "Aren't you exhausted?"

"Nope." He shook his head. "You've revitalized me." He snapped his trousers shut and paused to run his fingers teasingly along her body, picking out a trail just below her navel and tracing a line between her breasts. "Of course, if you keep lying around like that, I might be tempted to forget about everything else until morning."

C.J. pulled herself up, knowing she didn't have the energy to survive another match with him. "I'm up, I'm up," she muttered, trying to pull herself together.

"So am I," he murmured, handing C.J. her discarded underwear.

She took it from him, puzzled. "Where are we going?" She had thought he wanted to stay there all night. She felt disappointment nibbling into her happiness.

"Home." The look he gave her was one of raw desire. "I want you in my bed. I want to make love to you until I'm ready to drop from sheer exhaustion. And—" he kissed her temple quickly "—I want a pair of clean underwear to put on in the morning."

"What about my underwear?" she wanted to know.

His eyes raked over her, hot and wanting. "You look best without any."

She'd been right again. The interview did give his career a boost in the right direction. Riding the crest created by being "this year's hunk," Travis had been passed over by producers who were interested in serious actors for their films, not just faces. Now a story run on him in a weekly magazine that kept tabs on a host of celebrities both in and out of the business hinted that perhaps there was something more to Travis McQuade than a bright, gleaming smile and a perfect physique. She grabbed it off the newsstand just before she arrived at the studio.

"See, I told you," C.J. said, waving the magazine in the air as she walked onto the set. She dropped it in his lap as he sat nursing a cup of coffee. "Read that when you get a chance," she urged. "They're beginning to think of you as something other than just a pretty face and rippling muscles." Her enthusiasm was building, as was the pitch of her voice. "Now I'll get Berenstein on the line for you, and you can tell him—"

"Clem, stop," he ordered. She was beginning to crowd him again, he thought. It was up to him to make the decisions about that, not her.

She blew her bangs off her forehead, annoyed. Where was his ambition? "How long are you going to play it safe?" she asked.

"How long are you going to be a harpy?" he countered.

"Kids, kids, put your gloves down," Grant said, coming up from behind and putting his bulk between them. "What's the matter?" He looked from one to the other, waiting for an answer.

"He won't call Berenstein." Her calm voice belied the frustration she felt. Didn't he see that he had to strike now? Next year might be too late. Next year might bring another hunk, a fresher, younger sacrifice, and he would be out on his ear, without credentials, without a future.

"Why should he call Berenstein?"

"I don't know," Travis said irritably. "She comes in waving a magazine and suddenly thinks I should tell my agent I'm ready to step into Laurence Olivier's shoes as soon as he takes them off."

"Not Olivier's," C.J. insisted. "Ian Carroll's."

"What?" Travis cried. Was she crazy? He didn't have a snowball's chance in hell of trying out for the same type of roles as Ian Carroll. The man, though only a few years older, had a brilliant screen career and was at the top of his field. He had starred in a broad spectrum of movies, almost always to smashing reviews. If Travis pretended to be in the same category as Carroll, people would laugh in his face for his gall.

C.J. took a deep breath and started at the beginning. "I just read it in *Variety*," she explained patiently. "Ian Carroll had to bow out of a picture he was going to make. Something about conflicting assignments. The play he's in has just been signed to an extended engagement, and he won't be able to show up when the picture goes into production. His role in *The Seeds of Promise* is going to be recast."

"You make it sound as if all I have to do is try on the glass slipper." Travis rose, and the magazine she had given him fell to the ground. "It's not that easy."

"It's not easy at all if you don't try." What was wrong with him? Why wouldn't he try to extend himself? She had always reached for the stars. Why did he want to stay earthbound?

"They won't consider me," Travis insisted. "Believe me, I know." He had tried to convince his agent to try to get him parts that had something to them, some meat, some bite. But Berenstein's answer was always the same—"Don't rock the boat. The public knows what it wants, and it wants you as the powerful, romantic hero." Berenstein's stand had begun to erode Travis's self-confidence. Maybe it *was* true. Maybe he *couldn't* play any parts other than those he had played. If he didn't try, he wouldn't have to actually face the fact.

C.J. wouldn't give up. "They'll consider you if you test for it. Big stars sometimes test for parts," she insisted. "I know the role and—"

"How do you know the role?" he asked suspiciously. What had she been doing behind his back now? What possessed her to spend all her time trying to manipulate him?

She could have told him that she had been keeping her eyes open for properties, that she had been looking for something for him to bid on in order to prove himself, that ever since she had watched his performance in *Here Comes Culhane*, she had been convinced of his potential. She could have, but she knew that her admission would make him balk again. He'd say something about her transgressing beyond her boundaries.

And she didn't want to hear it, didn't want to hear that he had pigeonholed her into a designated role in his life. She didn't feel like just his personal manager anymore. They meant something to each other, damn it, something that didn't come with boundaries.

"I just know it, that's all," she answered vaguely. "It's *right* for you. Why don't you call Berenstein?"

Grant shrugged when Travis looked in his direction. "Worth a shot, kid. What do you have to lose?"

"Your credibility, Travis. That's what you have to lose," Berenstein said, sitting on the edge of his chair as he took the call. He was the embodiment of the fast-talking Hollywood agent. He liked to play up to the image. But right now the image was playing up to him. He was getting tired of his client's laments. The man could be eating caviar three times a day on what he was bringing in as Paris Cassidy. What possessed these actors to want to change?

He had a desk¹oad of clients who would have killed, literally, for a chance to be in Travis McQuade's shoes.

"The picture's heavy. Some philosophical mumbo jumbo. It's a risk. What if it's a flop? Do you want to be associated with a flop? Play the odds, Travis. Do yourself a favor. Do *Walker!*" he urged. "*Walker!* is your speed, not some soul-searching garbage that was written by a writer with an ax to grind. Look," he said impatiently, "have I ever steered you wrong?"

"No." But you haven't steered yourself wrong, either, Travis thought. It's not me you're worried about. It's you.

"There, you see? Be smart. Sign for *Walker!* Forget about *Seeds*."

"No, Harry, I won't forget about it," Travis said doggedly. C.J. was watching him. He purposely turned his back on her, lowering his voice. "I want to test for the part."

"Test, schmest, you're too big for testing—"

"I want to test for it, Harry."

Berenstein began looking for his matches, his unlit cigar hanging from his mouth. "And they wonder why agents drink. Okay, okay, but don't come crying to me if they laugh you out of the projection room. You gotta stick with what you know."

"And if I stick with what I know, what happens ten years from now?" Travis demanded, tired of constantly having to fight with his agent. Lately he felt as if he were fighting everyone. The public for his privacy, C.J. for his space. Didn't it ever let up?

"Ten years? Travis, I'm worried about next week. Why are you talking ten years from now? The bomb could drop and we'd all be dead. Ten years, huh," he snorted.

"But if it doesn't drop, Harry, what then? I can't go on dodging bullets and burning rubber forever."

An exasperated sigh met Travis's ear. "I'll take care of you."

"No one takes care of me, Harry. I take care of myself. Get me that test."

"Yeah, sure, and while I'm at it, I'll try to sell them on using Little Orphan Annie for the remake of *Cleopatra*."

The phone went dead. Travis replaced the receiver quietly.

"Well?" C.J. asked uncertainly, searching Travis's face for a sign as to how the conversation had gone.

"I don't know." He walked away from her. He didn't want her probing him right now. He needed room to breathe.

"Will he get you that test or not?"

Travis didn't answer.

C.J. walked around to face him. "If he doesn't," C.J. said, "I think you should get a new agent. One who cares about you and isn't just trying to exploit you."

"I never liked actors who dumped the people who helped them get to the top. When Harry Berenstein found me, I was nothing. He made me."

"Nobody made you, Travis. You did it on your own. You know that. You've told me so yourself." She touched his arm, trying to make him look at her, trying to make him see that what she was saying was right.

"Do you remember several seasons ago," she went on when he remained silent, "when Pat Kelly walked

out on his series because of 'creative differences'?
They replaced him for half a season. Same role, same
dialogue, better-looking guy. The part fell flat. The
show fell in the Nielsens. Pat Kelly *made* that show,
just like you make *Paris Cassidy*. It's a cardboard
part, but you put life into it. You've got talent, Travis.
All it takes is someone to see it, that's all."

His nerves were stretched taut. He knew he was
going to demand that test. He also knew what it would
cost him if he fell flat on his face. The last thing in the
world he wanted was to discuss it. "Clem, stop nagging me," he said, walking out and slamming the
door.

Eleven

C.J. stood very still as Travis's words echoed over and over again in her mind.

Nagging him? Was that what she had been doing?

No, it wasn't nagging, she thought defensively. Her natural exuberance, her enthusiasm, might make it *seem* as if she was nagging, but that didn't mean that she had turned into a smothering, domineering... Her mind trailed off in confusion.

"Damn it, I did it for you!" she shouted at the door, frustrated.

Doubt began to cloud her mind. *Had* she overstepped the bounds of her position? Maybe. But only to improve her client's life.

"Her client." The words sounded so cold, so detached, and she had been neither. She was involved with Travis on every level. That had never happened before.

She had never been in love with a client before, either.

C.J. sank down in a chair, staring, but not seeing. A lot of things had happened with Travis that had never happened before.

She tried to rethink the past few weeks. *Had* she lost her objectivity? In her zeal to have him do what she thought best, had she practically taken him over? She didn't know. She couldn't defend herself properly. She just didn't know anymore.

A repentant smile touched her lips. You're not the only headstrong person, Travis McQuade. But I only do these things because I love you.

All right, so now what? she wondered. She thought of the look in his eyes. What had she seen there? Agony? Hatred? In her present state she didn't know.

Levelheaded Clementine Jean Parker was falling apart, she realized. Another first.

She needed to get away. She needed space to think, to sort out her thoughts. And, she thought with a disparaging sigh, he probably needed space from her. He had called her a "harpy." No doubt about it, he needed time away from her.

Nagging. She had nagged him. Oh, God, what had she allowed herself to become? She felt tears stinging her eyes. Astounded, she touched one as it trickled down her cheek. Tears. She hadn't cried since her mother had died, hadn't let anything get to her that badly.

She had to get away from here before she made a complete idiot of herself.

She didn't remember leaving the lot. Her mind went on automatic pilot as the rest of her grew numb. She vaguely recalled passing Grant. He had called after her, but his voice registered in her mind only after she had gotten to her car.

Overwork was part of the problem, she told herself as she drove home. And Travis was the rest of it. She sighed as she drove along Wilshire.

She should have taken the vacation she had planned just before accepting this job. She should have stuck to her guns when she quit. She would have done them both more good if she had. As a personal manager she was supposed to free her clients to pursue their careers without headaches. She wasn't supposed to create headaches, or make her clients feel trapped. Yet that was exactly what she seemed to have done with Travis. At least, he thought so, and that was all that mattered. She had been the one who had decided that he needed to go after more demanding roles, that he needed to break free of the mold he had been cast in. She had thought she was helping.

Maybe, she thought later as she pulled out a suitcase from the closet, maybe he didn't want anything more. Maybe he was happy just being the recipient of mash letters and empty adulation.

No, he wasn't like that, she argued. He wasn't.

How do you know what he's like? her little voice asked. He doesn't let you get close enough to know.

The suitcase slowly dropped to the floor. C.J. sank down on her sofa, closing her eyes. She didn't know anything anymore. She thought, felt, hoped, but didn't really *know*. She felt so drained, so tired, so numb. For a moment she just gave up, wishing herself into a dark oblivion, and then she fell asleep.

A knocking woke her. At first she thought it was just a throbbing headache. She had slept fitfully, dreaming strange dreams. And all the while she heard his voice, calling her. Even in her sleep he invaded her thoughts. She was right about getting away. She needed to.

C.J. sat up in the dark room. It was evening. She had fallen asleep.

She ran her hands over her face, trying to focus. Her head felt awful. And the pounding was...real. Someone was knocking. Knocking steadily. And loudly.

"Clem, open the damn door."

C.J. scrambled to her feet, stumbling against her suitcase. She pressed her cheek against the door. It felt cool. It was real. His voice was real. He was there. "What...what do you want?"

"For you to open the door, to begin with."

She put her hand on the doorknob and took a breath to steady herself. Her other hand spiked through her hair, pushing it back. Oh, well, so she looked a mess. She wasn't trying to impress him. She wasn't trying to do anything anymore. She had lost her sense of purpose, her sense of herself. All she wanted to do now was go away for a while and collect her thoughts.

C.J. swung open the door. "Yes?"

"For God's sake, don't sound like you've just opened the door to an encyclopedia salesman," he said as he walked in.

"I don't open the door to encyclopedia salesmen. I hate them."

"Do you hate me, too?" he demanded, turning to face her. She felt as if his eyes were burning into her brain, searing a path to her thoughts.

"What?" He had no right to ask her questions when her brain felt so fuzzy. "No. Why?"

"Then why are you leaving?" He nudged the fallen suitcase with his toe.

"Oh, that." She moved toward the light switch. She needed to bathe the room in light. She felt far too vulnerable in the dark with him.

"Yes, that." His hand covered hers just as she found the light switch. The light stayed off. He turned her around, his face serious as he searched hers. "Have I done that to you, Clem? Have I frightened you off?"

"No," she insisted fiercely, perhaps too fiercely. "I just thought that, well... Look," she started again, "if I was...nagging—" she bit off the word "—I'm sorry." She looked at the floor. "I've never done anything like that before. Maybe you're right. Maybe I was getting too intense, too involved in aspects of your life I have no business touching. I thought...I'd get away for a while," she said, drawing the words out. "Do us both some good. I..." She tried to turn away, but he wouldn't let her.

Damn it, I'm going to cry again, she thought, angry at herself for the sign of weakness. Angry at him for bringing it out.

"I can give you the name of someone good if you want another personal manager," she offered tonelessly as she turned away.

His voice was hard. "I don't want the name of another personal manager."

"Oh." She swallowed. "Well..."

His fingers tightened on her shoulders. "I've already got the best."

She turned back, looking at him in surprise. "But I'm going away."

"The hell you are."

"Travis," she pleaded, feeling desperate. Why wouldn't he let her do this gracefully? "I got in too deep. I..."

He kissed her cheek, where a lone tear slid down. She thought she had never felt anything so tender in her life. It made her want to cry again.

"We both did," he told her.

"What's that supposed to mean?"

He cupped her face in his hands, lowering his until it was achingly close. She felt his breath against her skin as he spoke. "It means that this time when you left, I didn't want to go out and get a tree."

"I don't have room for another one," she said, weakly clinging to the conversation. Being so close to him was making her waver. Could she exist without him? Yes, but that was all she was going to do. Exist.

"This time I wanted to give you me." He paused and searched her face. "You don't realize what that means, do you?"

"Yes," her throat felt dry. "Of course I do."

His lips teased hers for a moment as he kissed her. "No," he said, "you don't." His hands dropped from her face, and he took her hand in his, drawing her over to the sofa. "Come here," he told her. "We have to talk."

As if I have a choice, she thought, sitting down next to him. She was his to do with as he would.

Travis put his arm around her, pulling her closer. The sofa rocked to and fro. "Rather fitting," he quipped, glancing down at the dark upholstery. "I've felt all at sea for a long time." Then he smiled at her upturned face. "I've been so busy guarding my territory that it blinded me to a lot of things."

"Such as?"

"Such as knowing that accepting help didn't mean that I was less of a man." He sighed. "It was so important to me to maintain control, to make my own decisions."

"I didn't try to make decisions for you," she protested. It was a reflexive action. She knew she had.

"No, you didn't try," he agreed. "You made them straight out."

"I—" The protest was only halfhearted.

"The haircut, the security system," he enumerated. "The—shall I go on?"

"No, you've made your point," she answered quietly, embarrassed. "And you're right. That's why I was going, because—"

He wouldn't let her finish. "Of course, the decisions you made were right."

She sat up, wriggling out of his grasp. His admission surprised her.

"I think the more right you were, the angrier I became. You see, I wanted to be in control. I wanted to make those decisions. You beat me to them. You were so in control, so collected, while I...I was—" he patted the sofa and it moved "—at sea, like I said. I felt like I was going in a hundred different directions and everyone was trying to pick up a piece of me. I wanted to save all the pieces and rebuild the old Travis McQuade.

"But," he said, shifting her so that she sat on his lap, "the old Travis McQuade wanted all this, dreamed about it in that dreary little house in Butte." He grew quiet for a moment as he looked at C.J. His eyes made love to her. She held her breath. "It's not such a bad life, I suppose, but I can't handle it without you."

"I—"

"Clem, don't argue with me. I've finally made a giant step toward becoming a better person. Don't ruin it."

She curled against him, slipping her arm behind his neck. "You couldn't become a better person than you already are."

"There you go." He sighed plaintively. "Arguing again."

"Just my nature, I guess."

"I like your nature," he told her, fondling her breast as he curled his arms around her. "I like all of you."

He kissed her, his lips soft and tender against her mouth. "Stay, Clem, stay."

She felt the warmth creeping into her veins. An exquisite yearning took hold. "Convince me."

"Whatever you say."

They made love slowly, gently, as if they were savoring every moment, every movement. Their clothes melted away, and they gloried in each other's bodies as if they were gifts that had been snatched away and then given back. C.J. adored the feel of his body against hers, the warmth, the pressure, the firm, hard outline that told her how much he wanted her. He really wanted her.

"Would it frighten you too much if I told you I loved you?" she asked, the words low and smoky in her throat.

"I don't know," he answered, his mouth busy tantalizing her quivering stomach. "Why don't you try and see?"

C.J. wound her fingers into his hair, closing her eyes in ecstasy as his burning mouth went lower, teasing the core of her femininity. Gently his hand parted her thighs, and his tongue sank in deep, deep, making it impossible for her to think, making her want him so fiercely that it seemed impossible that they had made love only a few short minutes ago.

"I . . . love . . . you," she gasped, arching into him, savoring all the incredible sensations that were bursting in her brain.

Exhausted, she gasped for air, realizing only vaguely that he was above her again, that his face was a scant inch away from hers. "No, no terror," he answered, as if they were carrying on a simple conversation, as if he wasn't driving her wild with desire. "I think I can handle it."

"Good," she breathed, entwining her arms around his neck. "Because I do. I love you, Travis McQuade, and I intend to go on loving you for the rest of my life."

"Shh." He put his finger to her lips. "No promises. Let's take it one step at a time."

She realized, even as their bodies merged as one again, that he hadn't said he loved her. But he was here, and he had opened himself up to her. That was enough for now.

His palms were sweating as he accepted the paper cup full of champagne that someone handed him. It was the season's wrap party. *Paris Cassidy, Man with a Gun* was over for the year. The cast and crew shared one final afternoon before they went their separate ways until the next season's filming brought them back together in July. They had already received word that the network was picking them up for another twenty-six episodes. No dealing in half measures. The network wanted the show for the entire season. *Paris* was as big a hit as ever.

The mood around Travis was highly festive, but his mind was elsewhere.

"Worried?" C.J. whispered, bringing her head close to his as she came up from behind.

He turned to smile at her. "I'd be lying if I said I wasn't."

The chair next to his was vacant, and she sat down. "You'll be great," she assured him.

"But will they see anyone besides Paris Cassidy?" he asked, cradling the paper cup between his hands.

Oh, I hope so, darling, she thought fervently. I hope so. "You'll make them see someone else."

He tried to draw courage from her eyes. A few days ago he would have upbraided himself for such "weakness." Now he realized that it was no sin to draw strength from another person, no shame to share yourself with someone. And C.J., in her unwavering loyalty, in her love, had become his strength.

His whole world had undergone a change in the past few days. Berenstein had finally, grudgingly, come through. Forecasting doom, the agent had arranged for a screen test. The producers of *The Seeds of Promise* had reluctantly agreed to let Travis take his shot.

"Probably want a good laugh," Berenstein had said, trying one last time to talk him out of his "foolishness" and into signing for *Walker!*

Travis had promised the man that if he failed the test, he would agree to do *Walker!* immediately.

"Money in the bank, kid, money in the bank," Berenstein had chirped, taking it as a foregone conclusion that Travis wouldn't get the other part.

No one, it seemed, had faith in him. No one but Clem.

He was smiling at her, she thought, and wondered why. He was preoccupied; she could see that. She wished she could reach in and—there you go again, she chided herself. Leave the man be.

He rose. It was time to go.

"I'll go with you," she offered.

"No," he said, and for a moment she felt as if he were shutting her out again. "I want to go alone."

He bent and quickly kissed her, drawing squeals from several onlookers. On the last day of shooting the studio had allowed Travis's fans in, held at bay, mercifully, by security guards. It was a way of promoting goodwill and steady patronage. The crowd encircled the entire soundstage. "Okay?" he asked, oblivious to everyone else in the area. He looked for understanding in her eyes.

"Okay." She tried her best to give him the most encouraging smile she could.

C.J. chewed on her nails as she paced her apartment.

"Damn," she muttered, looking down at the bitten off mess. She'd never chewed her nails. Not even as a child. "You certainly have had an effect on my life, Travis McQuade."

And what sort of an effect would he have later? What was she going to be to him later? Would she just continue as his personal manager, feeling the way she did about him? Or did they have a future?

She was searching for a commitment, she realized. But getting a commitment from Travis would be difficult. She had a feeling that she had gotten as much of a commitment as she was going to get from the man. And she wanted more.

"My God, the man is sweating out his life at this very moment, and you're trying to plan forever. Next thing you know, you'll be proposing to him."

She knew it was only half a joke. She was probably capable of doing just that. She was going to have to watch herself. One step at a time, he had said to her. Take it one step at a time.

When he knocked, she jumped, toppling the benjamina in her hurry to get to the door.

Her eyes scanned his face apprehensively as he came in. It was a complete mask. Had it gone badly? Had they laughed at him, just as he'd feared? Was he going to blame her for it? If it hadn't been for her, he wouldn't have tried. Guilt seized her.

"Well, *say* something!" she cried, shutting the door behind him.

Instead of answering her, he walked over to the fallen benjamina. "What happened to the tree?"

She pushed past him, grasping the pot and setting it upright again. "I was in such a hurry to get to the door, I knocked it over." She scooped the fallen dirt from her floor and back into the pot. He bent down to help her. "So tell me already. What happened?" She dusted off her hands against the back of her jeans.

"I read for it," he told her, rising.

"And? And?" She got back to her feet and clutched at his shirt. "You have the ability to make me crazy, do you know that?"

"The feeling," he answered, brushing his lips sensuously against hers, "is mutual. As a matter of fact—" he took her into his arms and kissed her again "—you're doing it right now."

Another kiss followed. She tried to keep her mind on the test, but it was getting harder and harder to do so. Was he seeking refuge in her arms, or was he celebrating? In either case, at least he didn't blame her. He couldn't be kissing her like this and holding a grudge at the same time. Nobody was that good an actor.

C.J. kissed him back. Her fingers wedged between them as she began opening the buttons on his shirt. "They didn't laugh, did they?"

"No," he said, a smile in his eyes, "they didn't laugh. I think I impressed them."

She peeled his shirt away and slipped her hands along his muscular chest. "You certainly impress me," she said softly.

He lifted her up into his arms. "I fully intend to, Clem. I fully intend to."

Twelve

———

"So it went well?" It was more of a statement than an actual question on C.J.'s part. She could sense that it had by the way he had made love to her.

They were lying in her bed, surrounded by the soft, contented afterglow of lovemaking. She propped herself up, resting her arm on his chest as she waited for him to answer.

"It went well," he told her.

"And they didn't laugh?" C.J. grinned, an I-told-you-so look on her face.

"They didn't laugh."

"McQuade," she whispered coyly as she traced designs along the muscular ridges of his lower abdomen, "if I had wanted an echo, I would have gone mountain climbing. *Talk* to me." Her eyes began to gleam mischievously as she skimmed her hand lower, just barely touching him with her palm, her cool fingers feathering along a path guaranteed to drive him out of his mind. "Or I'll torture you."

He moved so quickly that he took her totally by surprise. Within an instant she was on her back, pinned flat against the bed by the weight of his body. He grinned triumphantly at her. "You're already torturing me." He touched her lips lightly with his finger, making her tingle. "As for the test, I think I really surprised them. I'm not sure what strings Berenstein pulled in order to set it up, but when I started, I got the distinct impression that they were only going through the motions." He began to smile broadly. It was the smile of a man who felt he had taken an important step. "Until I started reading. I may not have gotten the part, but I made them sit up and listen."

"I knew you had it in you." Did her adoration show in her face? she wondered. Did he know how special he was to her? How much he mattered?

He had some doubts of his own. Did she love him as he was, or for what she thought he could become? He framed her face with his hands. There was no other way to find out. He had to ask. "Will it bother you if I don't get the part?"

She turned her head emphatically from side to side, her silken hair brushing against his hands. "Not if it doesn't bother you. It only bothered me that you didn't want to try," she told him honestly. "Travis?"

Her voice was sweet, low. He loved the way she said his name. It made her sound vulnerable, wanting. It was exactly the way he felt around her.

"Hmm?" He began to nibble on the outer shell of her ear. She wriggled beneath him with excitement and anticipation, her movements arousing him in turn. She could see it in his eyes.

"I'm really sorry if I got too...well, you know. Pushy."

His eyes smiled, the dim light of the moon highlighting the sparkle. "No, you're not. You're naturally pushy. I bet you didn't leave home. Your brothers probably rode you out on a rail."

"They were sorry to see me go." She pretended to sniff. She knew he was teasing her. Teasing her in more ways than one. He started to kiss her neck and continued downward until he was applying gentle little kisses all around her breasts. He was making her ache for him again. Would her needs ever be satisfied? If she was very, very lucky, she'd spend eternity finding out.

"Why *did* you leave home?" He found himself wanting to know things about her. Every last detail.

It was hard to remember, hard to think, when he was this close to her, nude. She yearned to make love again, not conversation. What had happened to her since she had met him?

"To conquer new horizons," she finally answered. "To be needed, I guess. My brothers were mostly grown and fiercely independent." She let her hand stray over his hair. "Kind of like you."

"Do you like being needed?" The question reverberated along the taut skin of her abdomen, making it quiver even more.

How did he expect her to think when he was making her crazy? He knew what he was doing, she thought. His onslaught stopped for a second, and he rested his head against her stomach. She could feel his breath tickling her. She tried hard to concentrate.

"Yes and no. I need a purpose, but I don't want to be shackled. That's why I never stay long in one place, just until I feel my job is done. Until everything is set in order. I guess maybe I'm a lot like you. I need freedom, too. Freedom to do whatever I want to." She let her voice drop as her eyes asked for forgiveness. "I should have understood that about you."

He raised his head, moving up to look at her face. "It's a bit more complex than that."

C.J. nodded. "I know, your fans—"

"Clem," he said with a sigh, "do you *always* have to be right? Have you ever thought of going for a degree in psychology?"

"I don't want to shrink heads," she said softly, touching his face. "I just want yours."

"On a silver platter?" he teased.

"No, on a pillow, next to mine."

His eyes made love to her before he did. "You already have that."

For now, she thought as his mouth took hers in an incredibly hungry kiss. And that was all she could ask of him.

"You want me to come with you?" C.J. asked, astounded. She felt a ray of sunshine spreading within her. He wanted her.

"Sure," Travis answered, putting his clothes on as he prepared to go home. The noonday sun was highlighting her bedroom. They had spent the entire morning in a lovers' paradise. She hadn't expected it to go on.

She was afraid to let herself believe that he really wanted her along. "But there won't be anything for me to do. Professionally, I mean. You'll be on vacation."

The look he gave her told her that there would be *plenty* for her to do in an *un*professional capacity. "What kind of a vacation would it be if I'm off at my cabin and you're here?"

He stopped what he was doing and came up behind her. Weaving his strong hands about her waist, he leaned his head against her, inhaling the gentle perfume of her hair. "Who knows, I might need some personal managing while I'm up there. Stranger things have happened."

C.J. laughed, putting her hands over his. She loved the way he touched her. It made her feel as if she belonged to him. And suddenly belonging, not independence, meant everything to her. "I'd love to come." Put to the test, she couldn't think of a thing that would make her happier.

"Good." He released her. "Having you there will balance out taking the script along."

She turned around so she could see his face. "Script?" Had he kept it from her? Had he actually gotten the part yesterday?

"I'm taking *Walker!* up with me." He tried to sound casual about it.

She could see that it didn't make him happy. "Oh?"

"Well, I've only got a limited amount of free time to make a movie. They go into production at the end of the month," he said matter-of-factly.

She began to button his open shirt, starting from the bottom. Don't sound judgmental, she warned herself. She didn't want to create another rift. "Shouldn't they have gotten a leading man by now?"

"They're banking on me."

"Have you signed?"

"No, but I promised Berenstein I would if nothing came of my test for *Seeds*. It wouldn't hurt to go over the part." He sounded almost resigned to his fate.

She knew she should keep quiet, but she was too in love with him not to risk things. She *knew* he didn't want to do this picture. She could *feel* it. "It's only been, what? Twelve hours since the test?"

"Less," he said, reaching for his slacks and pulling them on. "They said they'd make their decision for the part by the end of the week. So," he said, taking her hand and bringing it to his lips, "we have nearly a week not to think about anything but ourselves. How about it? Are you game?"

She looked radiant as she answered. "Always fair game for you."

When the word "idyllic" was formed, C.J. thought, lying on a bed of grass near a stream, watching Travis fish, whoever came up with it must have had something like this in mind. They had spent five days up here. Five days and nights that flowed into one another, laced with the passion and joy of lovemaking and discovering little things about each other. Things that they had in common. Being, for a change, totally in tune with each other.

C.J. sat up to get a better look at Travis. Up here, at his hideaway, he was all hers. Up here there were no problems to get in the way. He acted freer, happier.

Had anyone ever loved another human being as much as she loved him? she wondered.

A bee caught her eye. It was moving from one flower to another, lingering a moment at each before going on. That was her, she thought. That was how she had lived her life for the past five years. It had been what she had wanted at the time. It wasn't what she wanted now.

Marry me, she thought, staring at his broad back.

Travis turned around. "What?"

To her horror, she realized that she had said the words aloud. "I said, 'Watch out for the bee.'"

That was close. He already thought she was pushy. What would he say if he knew what she'd actually said? She was going to have to watch herself.

Travis propped the fishing pole between two rocks, then moved over toward her. "Let the bee watch out for himself. I'd rather watch you."

"I'm not doing anything." She laughed.

He caressed her face, tilting her chin back to meet his lips. "Yet," he told her, sampling the nectar he found there. "Hmmm, better not let the bee know how sweet you taste. He won't leave you alone."

C.J. lay down on the grass, her arms around his neck. "So long as you don't, that's all that matters."

He kissed her forehead lightly, sending a tremor of anticipation through her. "Not a chance, Clem, not a chance."

She felt his hand delve beneath her cotton pullover, his fingers cupping her breast. Slowly the material inched its way upward.

"Aren't you afraid someone will see us?" she asked, barely caring whether or not there was anyone around.

"This is private land. I own it," he reminded her.

"Like your shower," she said playfully, remembering the look of adoration on the teenager's face when she had seen Travis.

"If I wait until we get back to the cabin, I might just shrivel up from wanting you." He tugged at the snap of her shorts.

She tried to maintain a serious expression. "I wouldn't want to be responsible for that. Your public would kill me."

"Right," he murmured. His breath tickled her neck. "Just hold that thought."

"I'd rather hold you."

"Demands, demands." A ring of kisses began depleting her strength. "You are the most demanding female I ever met."

"And?" she breathed.

His voice was low, husky. It thrilled her. "And I want to make love to you very, very badly."

She shook her head slowly. "You can't do that."

"What?" What was she up to?

"You couldn't make love badly if you tried, McQuade. It isn't in you."

She felt his smile against her skin. "Let's put it to the test."

"Let's."

This was ridiculous. She refused to be sad just because they were leaving. It was totally unlike her.

But who was she lately?

She had changed from the effervescent, competent but distant woman she had been when she'd come into his life. She had become Travis McQuade's woman for however long he wanted her. Guarding his independence so zealously, he had made her surrender hers. She no longer wanted the things that had mattered to her. All she wanted was him.

And to remain in this room, loving him until she died in his arms.

Not a very logical thought, C.J., her mind said tauntingly.

She sat on the edge of the warm, double bed that had held them for half the time they were there. Travis was packing his suitcase. She watched him drop the script for *Walker!* on top. He had barely glanced at it for days.

"I'm going to do it," he said, his voice hollow.

She nodded. She knew what this was costing him. He was admitting defeat.

"After all, it's a movie." It hadn't been all that long ago that no one would offer him a movie at all, he thought.

"No arguing with that," she said quietly.

"And it's the same formula that's been so successful for me."

"Can't mess with success." She was trying to sound positive for his sake. She had no right to let her own feelings about the matter show. He had made his decision, and he had the right to do that, no matter what she thought.

"I have to face it, Clem, maybe this is all there is for me."

She shook her head. "I can't accept that." *Shut your mouth, C.J.* "You're too good."

He let the suitcase lid drop from his fingers, then turned to her, taking her into his arms. "Don't you think that's a slightly prejudiced remark?"

"No." She shook her head positively. "I thought you had talent even when I thought you were an ornery son of a bi—gun," she amended at the last minute with an intentionally innocent grin.

"Oh, you did, did you?"

"Yes."

"Thought I was a bastard, did you?"

"At times."

He nodded, accepting that. A twinkle entered his eyes. "I won't tell you what I thought of you."

"Don't." She snuggled against him. "I think it's better that way."

He felt his need for her take over again. A need that would always be there. Would *she* always be there? *Ask her.* "Clem, will you—"

"What?" she prodded, trying to hide her impatience when he stopped talking.

No, not now. Not yet. "Will you start up the car?" he asked, fishing out his keys. He handed them to her. "I'll get your suitcase."

"Sure." Disappointment laced the word.

She straightened her shoulders and walked to the door.

They rode back in silence.

And here's the real world, she thought as they walked up the driveway.

A clanging of bells went off as he opened the front door.

"You've tripped the alarm," C.J. said loudly.

"No kidding," he said, raising his voice and fumbling with the switch that turned the system off. "Don't know what I'd do without you to advise me."

Was he being testy, or just teasing? She saw tension in his face. Were they going to wind up sparring again?

No, it wasn't her this time, she realized. She wasn't the one irritating him. They had gone all through that. It was his decision that was bothering him. He didn't want to do that script, no matter what he said to the contrary. No matter how much either one of them pretended.

She still heard ringing. "What's that?" she asked, looking at the alarm.

"That's the phone," he realized, dropping their suitcases inside the front door.

"Couldn't even wait until you got in the door," she muttered under her breath. It was starting again, the demands on his time, the pressure.

She wasn't going to think about anything. C.J. forced herself not to listen to his conversation, and walked into the kitchen. She was going to hunt up something for them to eat and then go home.

When he walked into the kitchen several minutes later, he had an odd expression on his face.

"What's the matter?" C.J. asked, wiping her hands on a paper towel. She crossed over to him.

"That was Berenstein."

"And?" Why did she always have to pry words out of him?

"They called him about the test."

The all powerful "they," she thought, bracing herself, searching for words to comfort him with. He couldn't have gotten the part. He didn't look happy.

"Well, what did they say?"

"I got it."

His voice was quiet, full of stunned disbelief.

"You got it?" she cried, throwing her arms around him. "McQuade, that's wonderful! I'm so proud of you!" She rained kisses on his face, then stopped. "Wait," she said, just before he moved to kiss her back. "Something's wrong, isn't it?"

"Berenstein honestly believes I'll ruin my image with this picture."

"I see." And he was wrestling with himself. What should she do? Should she urge him to play it safe? To give up something that could change his life? Or should she urge him to grab it? To do something that might, as Berenstein said, shatter the pretty boy image? Well, would that be so bad? She held her words in check. She knew what she wanted to say. She also knew what she *had* to say.

"What do you want to do?"

"I want to make it," he admitted, his voice growing in intensity. "I want to make that picture so bad that it hurts inside. I read that script, Clem, and you were right. It *is* me, more me than those two dimensional he-men I've been playing."

She stood on her toes and put her hands on his shoulders. "So follow your heart, Travis," she whispered. *"Do it."*

He threw back his head and laughed. "She's right again, God help me. I will do it." He looked like a man freed of his own private devil. Travis picked her up and spun her around until she was dizzy. "I'll do it, and damn the consequences. I'll do it."

When he set her down, she felt unsteady. He captured her mouth, pressing her against him, before she had a chance to draw a clean breath. Her dizziness grew.

"We've got to pack. They're going on location in a week."

"Are you sure you want to take me along?" she asked. This was something new for him. Maybe having her along would act as a millstone. Maybe—

"Are you ever going to stop questioning what I say, Clem?"

She shrugged. "Maybe."

"I suppose you're going to want to leave out the part about 'obey.'"

She held up her hand. Did he mean . . . ? Could he possibly be saying . . . ? "Wait a minute. You're going too fast here."

"Me?" he asked innocently, feigning shock. "*I* am going too fast for *you*?"

"I can do without the smart remarks," she said wryly.

"But I can't do without you," he said, taking hold of her arms and pulling her close. She fit against him so well, he thought. The other half of his soul.

"What about 'obey'?" she prodded.

"You won't, will you?"

"Won't what? McQuade, you're talking in circles."

"I've had a good teacher."

"Will you tell me what you're trying to say?" she demanded impatiently, hope nipping at her.

"I'm guessing that you'll want the minister to leave out the part about obeying me." The look on his face was pure innocence as he toyed with her hair.

"*What* minister?"

"The minister who's going to marry us. He's about seventy-three now, I think. Funny-looking little man. I used to think he was a gnome when I was growing up."

She put her hands to his mouth, stopping him. "Are you asking me to marry you?"

"In a roundabout way, yes."

"Very roundabout," she said, laughing.

"Well, will you?"

"What do you think?"

"I think," he said, kissing her lower lip, then her upper one, then letting his kiss flower into something deep that left them both wanting more, "that I'm going to have a hell of an exciting life ahead of me."

"Travis?" she asked as his lips trailed along her throat.

He knew that tone. Something was on her mind. "Yes?"

"Am I still going to be your personal manager?"

He laughed. "Could anything stop you?"

"Yes," she said quietly, gliding her fingertips along his lips. "You."

He smiled, kissing her fingers before she pulled them back. "Nice to know. But I like having the best." His eyes shone. "Except . . ."

"Except what?" she asked anxiously.

"I don't know if I can take your being right all the time."

C.J. grinned. "I'll try to make a mistake once in a while."

"Ah, something to live for." He caressed her face. "Oh, by the way."

"Yes?"

"Did I happen to mention that I love you very, very much?"

"No. Mention it. Mention it."

"I'll do better than that. I'll show you."

Silhouette Desire

COMING NEXT MONTH

WILLING SPIRIT
Erin Ross

Sir Christopher Burke was as magnificently
handsome as a medieval warrior. With a fierceness
born of overpowering desire he invaded, he
ravaged, he plundered…but would he conquer
Athena's deepest passions?

THE BLOND CHAMELEON
Barbara Turner

Delancy O'Brien was a skilled impersonator. She
could be anyone, it seemed, but herself — now that
she'd met Stuart Thorne. But Stuart seemed
determined to catch more than just a glimpse of the
real Delancy O'Brien.

CAJUN SUMMER
Maura Seger

Once everyone had thought that Arlette would
marry Julian, but she had put an end to that by
leaving. Now she was back and Julian was still
single, still attractive and more determined than
ever.

Silhouette Desire

SEPTEMBER TITLES

EYE OF THE TIGER
Diana Palmer

DECEPTIONS
Annette Broadrick

HOT PROPERTIES
Suzanne Forster

LAST YEAR'S HUNK
Marie Nicole

PENNIES IN THE FOUNTAIN
Robin Elliott

CHALLENGE THE FATES
Jo Ann Algermissen

Silhouette Special Edition

SEPTEMBER TITLES